300 BEST SELLING HOME PLANS

No. 34602
Family Get-Away

■ This plan features:
— Three bedrooms
— Two and one half baths

■ A wrap-around porch for views and visiting provides access into the Great Room and Dining area

■ A spacious Great Room with a two-story ceiling and dormer window above a massive fireplace

■ A combination Dining/Kitchen with an island work area and breakfast bar opening to a Great Room and adjacent to the laundry/storage and half-bath area

■ A private two-story Master Bedroom with a dormer window, walk-in closet, double vanity bath and optional deck with hot tub

■ Two additional on the second floor bedrooms sharing a full bath

FIRST FLOOR — 1,061 SQ. FT.
SECOND FLOOR — 499 SQ. FT.
BASEMENT — 1,061 SQ. FT.

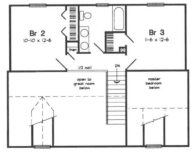

Br 2
10-10 x 12-6

Br 3
11-6 x 12-6

1/2 hall

DN

open to great room below

master bedroom below

Second Floor Plan

Optional Deck w/ Hot Tub

privacy fence

crawl space access

storage

Master Br

Alternate Foundation Plan

TOTAL LIVING AREA:
1,560 SQ. FT.

No materials list available

No. 34602

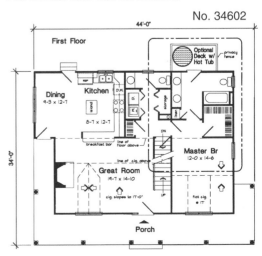

44'-0"

First Floor

Optional Deck w/ Hot Tub
privacy fence

Dining
9-3 x 12-7

Kitchen

8-7 x 12-7

breakfast bar

line of floor above

line of clg. above

34'-0"

Great Room
14-7 x 14-10

clg. slopes to 17'-0"

storage

DN

Master Br
12-0 x 14-6

UP

flat clg. 8 FT

Porch

No. 10785

Farmhouse Flavor

■ This plan features:

— Three bedrooms

— Two and one half baths

■ A inviting wrap-around porch with old fashioned charm

■ Two-story foyer

■ A wood stove in Living Room that warms the entire house

■ A Modern Kitchen flowing easily into bayed Dining Room

■ A first floor Master Bedroom with private Master Bath

■ Two additional bedrooms with walk-in closets and cozy gable sitting nooks

FIRST FLOOR — 1,269 SQ. FT.
SECOND FLOOR — 638 SQ. FT.
BASEMENT — 1,269 SQ. FT.

TOTAL LIVING AREA: 1,907 SQ. FT.

Slab/Crawl Space Option

Deck

Living Rm 13 x 19-6

W | D
Ldry

wood stove

Kitchen 11 x 12

MBr 1 13-6 x 14

DN

Dining Rm 12-10 x 13-6

Foyer

39'-0"

47'-0"

First Floor

slope

skylight

open to below

Balcony

slope

slope

Br 2 10-4 x 14

DN

Br 3 11 x 14

plant ledge

slope

No. 10785

A Karl Kreeger Design

No. 20165
Classic Drama

■ This plan features:

— Three bedrooms

— Two and one half baths

■ A central Foyer, crowned by a balcony sloping upward to meet the high ceiling of a fireplaced Living Room

■ A sky lit Dining Room with three-sided view of the adjoining Deck

■ A gourmet Kitchen with built-in desk and an abundance of cabinet space

■ Master Bedroom offering a sloping ceiling, walk-in closet and luxurious bath

■ Generous closet and storage space throughout the home

FIRST FLOOR — 901 SQ. FT.
SECOND FLOOR — 864 SQ. FT.
BASEMENT — 901 SQ. FT.
GARAGE — 594 SQ. FT.

**TOTAL LIVING AREA:
1,765 SQ. FT.**

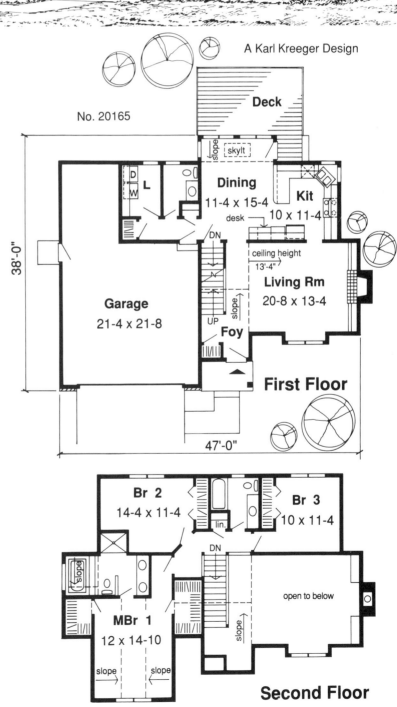

A Karl Kreeger Design

No. 20165

38'-0"

47'-0"

Deck

skylt

D
W   L

Dining
11-4 x 15-4

Kit
10 x 11-4

desk

ceiling height
13'-4"

DN

Garage
21-4 x 21-8

Living Rm
20-8 x 13-4

UP

slope

Foy

First Floor

Br 2
14-4 x 11-4

lin.

Br 3
10 x 11-4

DN

open to below

slope

MBr 1
12 x 14-10

slope   slope

Second Floor

No. 24400
National Treasure

■ This plan features:

— Three bedrooms

— Two and one half baths

■ A wrap-around covered porch

■ Decorative vaulted ceilings in the fireplaced Living room

■ A large Kitchen with central island/breakfast bar

■ A sun-lit sitting area

FIRST FLOOR — 1,034 SQ. FT.
SECOND FLOOR — 944 SQ. FT.
BASEMENT — 944 SQ. FT.
GARAGE & STORAGE — 684 SQ. FT.

**TOTAL LIVING AREA:
1,978 SQ. FT.**

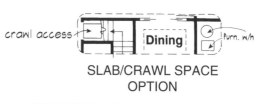

crawl access

Dining

Furn. w/h

SLAB/CRAWL SPACE
OPTION

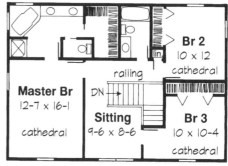

Br 2
10 x 12
cathedral

Master Br
12-7 x 16-1
cathedral

railing

DN

lin.

Sitting
9-6 x 8-6

Br 3
10 x 10-4
cathedral

SECOND FLOOR

FIRST FLOOR

No. 24400

39'-6"

BOOKS

Living
21-2 x 12-4
decor clg.

Kitchen
14-11 x 12-4

DW

W
D

Storage/Shop
16-2 x 12-7

**Den/
Guest**
10 x 10

Dining
10 x 12-3
decor clg.

Garage
23-2 x 19-3

67'-6"

An Upright Design

4

No. 10012

Rustic Design Blends into Hillside

■ This plan features:

— Three bedrooms

— Two and one half baths

■ A redwood deck that adapts equally to both lake and ocean settings

■ A Family Room measuring 36 feet long and leading out to a shaded patio

■ Fireplaces in both the Living Room and Family Room

■ An open Kitchen with a laundry room for convenience

FIRST FLOOR — 1,198 SQ. FT.
BASEMENT — 1,198 SQ. FT.

TOTAL LIVING AREA:
1,198 SQ. FT.

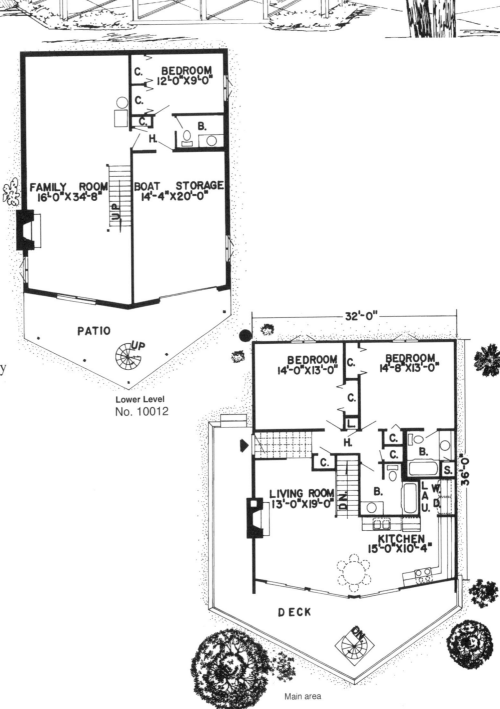

BEDROOM
12'-0"X9'-0"

C.
C.
C.
B.
H.

FAMILY ROOM
16'-0"X34'-8"

BOAT STORAGE
14'-4"X20'-0"

UP

PATIO

UP

Lower Level
No. 10012

32'-0"

BEDROOM
14'-0"X13'-0"

BEDROOM
14'-8"X13'-0"

C.
C.
L.
H.
C.
C.
B.
C.
S.

36'-0"

LIVING ROOM
13'-0"X19'-0"

DN
B.
LAU.
W. D.

KITCHEN
15'-0"X10'-4"

DECK

Main area

No. 20222

Modern Living with a Farmhouse Feel

■ This plan features:

— Four bedrooms

— Two full and one half baths

■ A large Living Room equipped with a fireplace

■ A well-equipped Kitchen that serves both the informal Breakfast Area and the formal Dining Room with equal ease

■ A cooktop island that doubles for a snack bar and a built-in pantry in the efficient Kitchen

■ A large walk-in closet and private Master Bath in the Master Suite

■ Three additional bedrooms, one with a walk-in closet, that share use of a full hall bath

FIRST FLOOR — 1,488 SQ. FT.
SECOND FLOOR — 893 SQ. FT.
BASEMENT — 801 SQ. FT.
GARAGE — 677 SQ. FT.

TOTAL LIVING AREA:
2,381 SQ. FT.

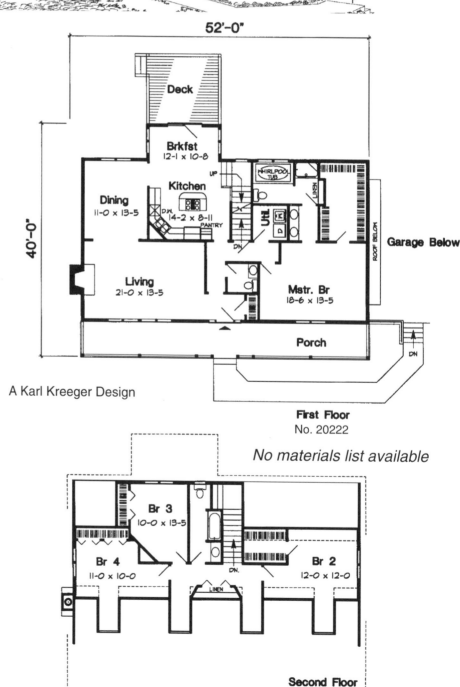

A Karl Kreeger Design

No materials list available

First Floor
No. 20222

Second Floor

6

No. 10220

Bedrooms Sliders Open Onto Wooden Deck

■ This plan features:

— Two bedrooms

— One full bath

■ A fifty foot deck setting the stage for a relaxing lifestyle encouraged by this home

■ A simple, yet complete floor plan centering around the large Family Area, warmed by a prefab fireplace with sliders to the deck

■ An efficient L-shaped Kitchen that includes a double sink with a window above, and direct access to the rear yard and the Laundry Room

■ Two bedrooms privately located, each outfitted with sliding doors to the deck and a large window for plenty of light

MAIN AREA — 888 SQ. FT.

TOTAL LIVING AREA: 888 SQ. FT.

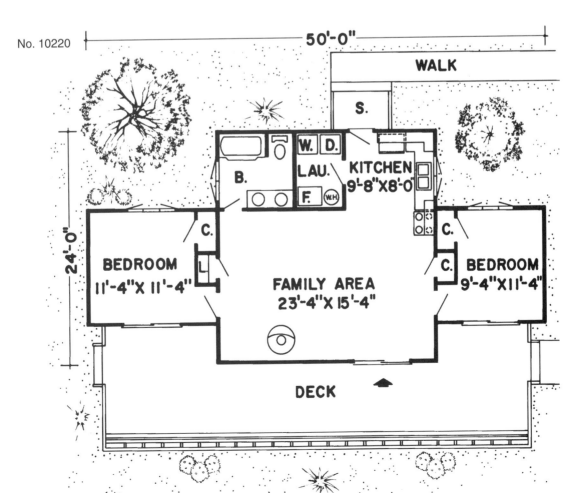

No. 93100
Stylish Single-Level

■ This plan features:

— Three bedrooms

— Two full and one half baths

■ A well-appointed, U-shaped Kitchen separated from the Dining Room by a peninsula counter

■ A spacious Living Room, enhanced by a focal point fireplace

■ An elegant Dining Room with a bay window that opens to a screen porch, expanding living space

■ A Master Suite with a walk-in closet and private Master Bath

■ Two family bedrooms that share a full hall bath

MAIN AREA — 1,642 SQ. FT.
GARAGE — 591 SQ. FT.
BASEMENT — 1,642 SQ. FT.

TOTAL LIVING AREA:
1,642 SQ. FT.

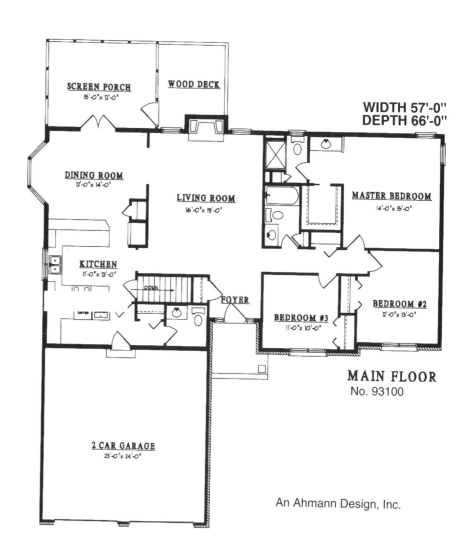

WIDTH 57'-0"
DEPTH 66'-0"

MAIN FLOOR
No. 93100

An Ahmann Design, Inc.

SCREEN PORCH
15'-0" x 12'-0"

WOOD DECK

DINING ROOM
12'-0" x 14'-0"

LIVING ROOM
16'-0" x 19'-0"

MASTER BEDROOM
14'-0" x 15'-0"

KITCHEN
11'-0" x 13'-0"

FOYER

BEDROOM #3
11'-0" x 10'-0"

BEDROOM #2
12'-0" x 13'-0"

2 CAR GARAGE
23'-0" x 24'-0"

No. 10417

Kitchen is Gourmet's Heaven

■ This plan features:
— Four bedrooms
— Five full baths
■ Cedar shake roofing which contrasts nicely with the brick exterior

■ Double entry doors ushering you into a two-story entrance with a curving staircase
■ Ten foot ceilings throughout the lower level, nine foot ceilings in the second level
■ A spacious Kitchen which will appeal to the gourmet cook in everyone

First floor — 3,307 sq. ft.
Second floor — 837 sq. ft.
Garage — 646 sq. ft.
Porch and patios — 382 sq. ft.

**Total living area:
4,144 sq. ft.**

No. 10417

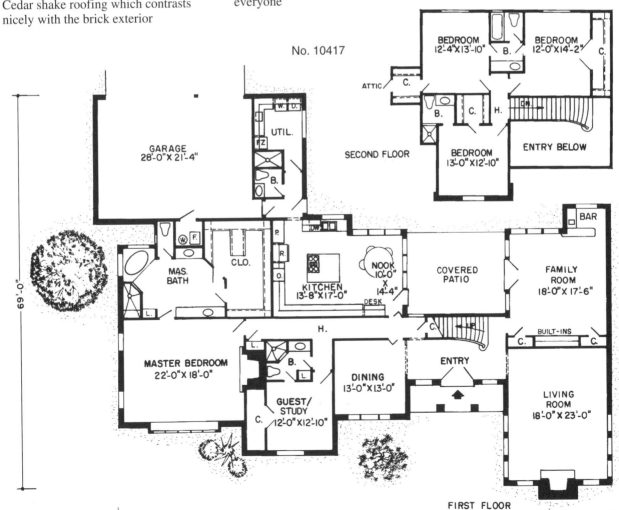

No. 24302

Champagne Style on a Soda-Pop Budget

■ This plan features:

— Three bedrooms

— Two full baths

■ Multiple gables, circle-top windows, and a unique exterior setting this delightful ranch apart in any neighborhood

■ Living and Dining Rooms flowing together to create a very roomy feeling

■ Sliding doors leading from the Dining Room to a covered patio

■ A Master Bedroom with a private bath

FIRST FLOOR — 988 SQ. FT.
BASEMENT — 988 SQ. FT.
GARAGE — 280 SQ. FT
OPTIONAL 2-CAR GARAGE — 384 SQ. FT.

TOTAL LIVING AREA:
988 SQ. FT.

Donald L. Marshall Architect

Basement Option

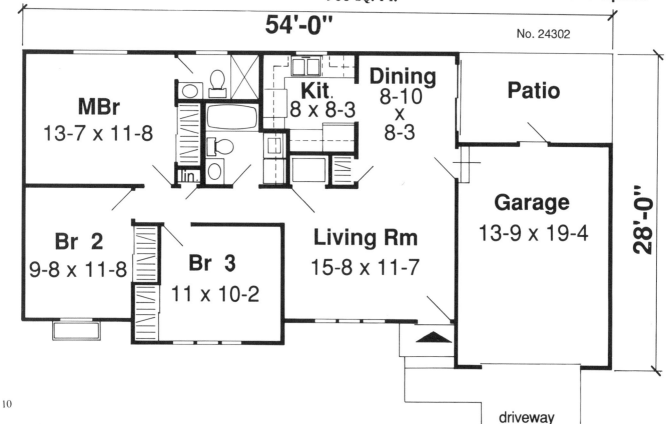

An Energetic Enterprises Design

No. 24256

Beautiful Combination of Old and New

■ This plan features:

— Three bedrooms

— Two full baths

■ Vaulted ceilings in the family living areas; Living Room, Dining Room, Family Room and Eating Nook

■ An open layout between the Kitchen, Nook, and Family Room, making the rooms appear even more spacious

■ A corner fireplace in the Family Room, which also has access to the patio

■ A peninsula counter in the island Kitchen that doubles as an eating bar

■ A lavish Master Suite that is equipped with a private bath and walk-in closet

■ Two family bedrooms that share a full hall bath

MAIN LIVING AREA — 2,108 SQ. FT.

TOTAL LIVING AREA:
2,108 SQ. FT.

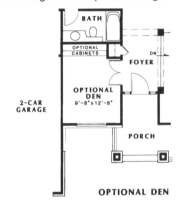

OPTIONAL DEN

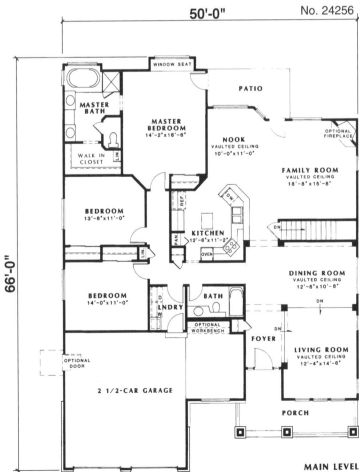

MAIN LEVEL

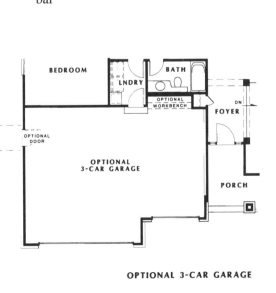

OPTIONAL 3-CAR GARAGE

No. 34043

A Home for Today and Tomorrow

■ This plan features:

— Three bedrooms

— Two full baths

■ An intriguing Breakfast nook off the Kitchen

■ A wide open fireplaced Living Room with glass sliders to deck

■ A step-saving arrangement of the Kitchen between the Breakfast and formal Dining Room

■ A handsome Master Bedroom with sky-lit compartmentalized bath

MAIN LIVING AREA — 1,583 SQ. FT.
BASEMENT — 1,583 SQ. FT.
GARAGE — 484 SQ. FT.

TOTAL LIVING AREA: 1,583 SQ. FT.

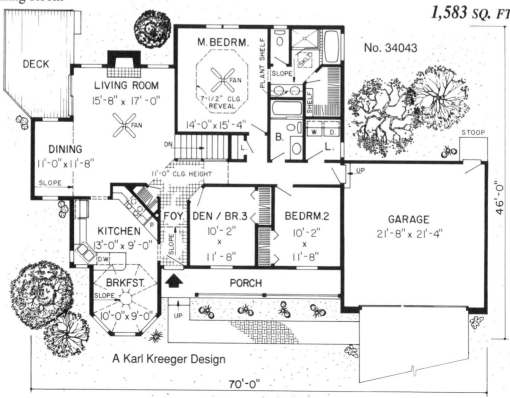

A Karl Kreeger Design

No. 10570
Ranch Design Utilizes Skylights

■ This plan features:

— Four bedrooms

— Two baths

■ A partial stone veneer front making this large ranch design very inviting

■ A large Library/Den next to the foyer sharing a two-way fireplace with the Living Room

■ A Living Room leading to a deck or screened porch

■ A very large hexagonal Kitchen with a connecting Dining Room

FIRST FLOOR — 2,450 SQ. FT.
BASEMENT — 2,450 SQ. FT.
GARAGE — 739 SQ. FT.

TOTAL LIVING AREA:
2,450 SQ. FT.

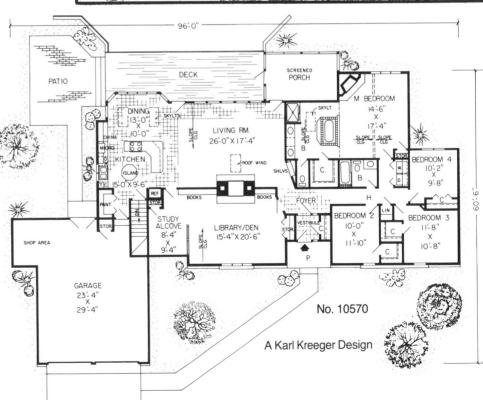

No. 10570

A Karl Kreeger Design

No. 10652

Two-Way Fireplace

■ This plan features:

— Three bedrooms

— Two and one half baths

■ A large Kitchen with cook-top island and a breakfast area opening to the deck

■ Built-in cedar closets and spacious bedrooms

■ A Master Suite loaded with a walk-in closet, skylight, double vanities and a sunken tub

■ A vaulted formal Dining Room and ceiling fans in the Kitchen and Living Room

FIRST FLOOR — 1,789 SQ. FT.
SECOND FLOOR — 568 SQ. FT.
BASEMENT — 1,789 SQ. FT.
GARAGE — 529 SQ. FT.

TOTAL LIVING AREA: 2,357 SQ. FT.

A Karl Kreeger Design

No. 10652

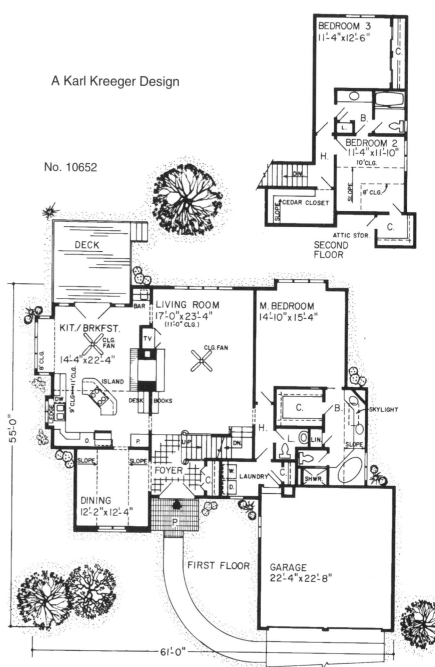

No. 34011

Windows Add Warmth To All Living Areas

■ This plan features:

— Three bedrooms

— Two full baths

■ A Master Suite with huge his and hers walk-in closets and private bath

■ Second and third bedroom with ample closet space

■ A Kitchen equipped with an island counter and flowing easily into the Dining and Family Rooms

■ A Laundry Room conveniently located near all three bedrooms

■ An optional garage

FIRST FLOOR — 1,672 SQ. FT.
OPTIONAL GARAGE — 566 SQ. FT.

TOTAL LIVING AREA: 1,672 SQ. FT.

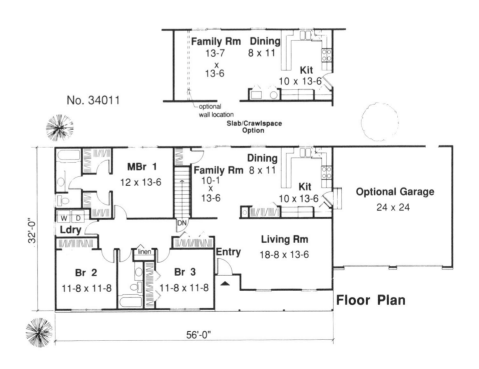

Family Rm 13-7 x 13-6

Dining 8 x 11

Kit 10 x 13-6

optional wall location

Slab/Crawlspace Option

No. 34011

MBr 1 12 x 13-6

Family Rm 10-1 x 13-6

DN

Dining 8 x 11

Kit 10 x 13-6

Optional Garage 24 x 24

W D

Ldry

linen

Living Rm 18-8 x 13-6

Br 2 11-8 x 11-8

Br 3 11-8 x 11-8

Entry

32'-0"

56'-0"

Floor Plan

No. 10334

Master Suite Crowns Outstanding Plan

■ This plan features:

— Four bedrooms
— Three and one half baths

■ A Master Suite with a Study, a walk-in closet, and lavish whirlpool bath

■ A Basement level which includes a Family Room with access to the patio via sliding doors

■ A two-car Garage with access to the utility room which contains a washer/dryer area and a half bath

■ A spacious Great Room with a massive fireplace and bow windows

First floor — 1,742 sq. ft.
Second floor — 809 sq. ft.
Lower floor — 443 sq. ft.
Basement — 1,270 sq. ft.
Garage — 558 sq. ft.

TOTAL LIVING AREA:
2,994 SQ. FT.

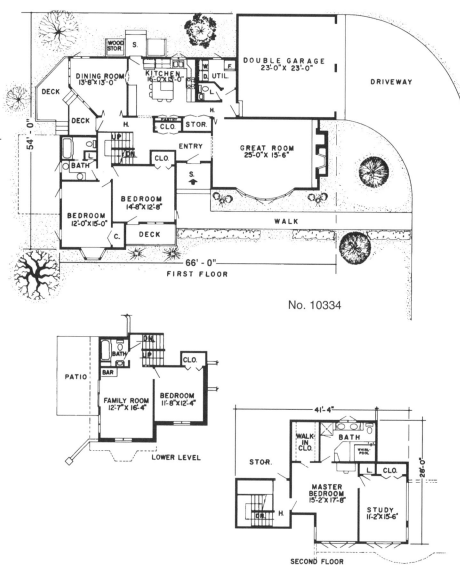

No. 10334

No. 10768

Upper Deck Affords Roadside View

■ This plan features:

— Five bedrooms

— Two and one half baths

■ A wetbar in the Family Room, built-in seating in the Breakfast Room, and an island Kitchen with a planning desk and room-sized pantry

■ A magnificent Master Suite including a fireplace, access to a private deck, an abundance of closet space and a tub in a bow window setting

FIRST FLOOR — 2,573 SQ. FT.
SECOND FLOOR — 2,390 SQ. FT.
BASEMENT — 1,844 SQ. FT.
CRAWL SPACE — 793 SQ. FT.
GARAGE — 1,080 SQ. FT.

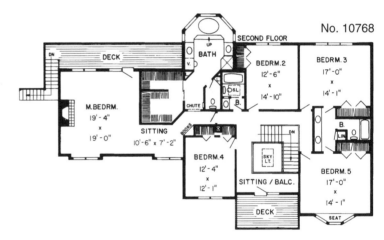

No. 10768

TOTAL LIVING AREA:
4,963 SQ. FT.

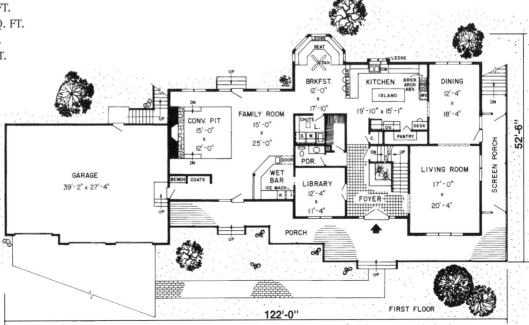

No. 20055
Outdoor-Lovers Dream

■ This plan features:

— Three bedrooms

— Two and one half baths

■ Sloped ceilings

■ An efficient Kitchen with cooktop peninsula and easy access to Breakfast or Dining Room

■ A Master Suite featuring soaring ceilings and a private dressing area flanked by a full bath and walk-in closet

■ A large Living room that adjoins a deck

FIRST FLOOR — 928 SQ. FT.
SECOND FLOOR — 773 SQ. FT.
BASEMENT — 910 SQ. FT.
GARAGE — 484 SQ. FT.

TOTAL LIVING AREA:
1,701 SQ. FT.

A Karl Kreeger Design

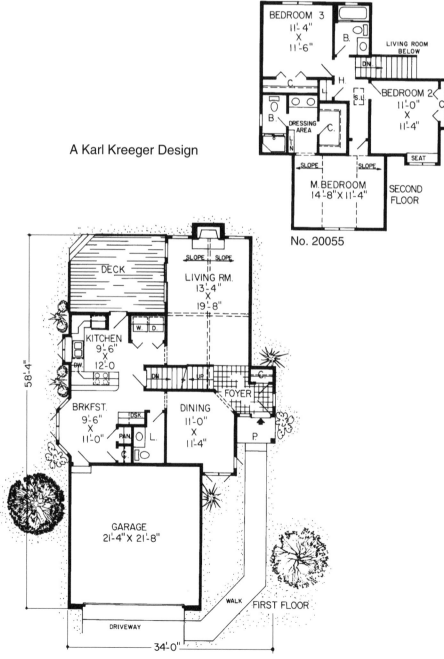

No. 20144
Country Comforts

■ This plan features:

— Four bedrooms

— Three full and one half bath

■ A sprawling front porch

■ A two-way fireplace warming the Hearth Room and the Living Room

■ A formal, bayed Dining Room with decorative ceiling

■ An efficient, well-appointed Kitchen with peninsula counter and double sinks

■ A vaulted ceiling in the Master Suite which is equipped with a private Master Bath

■ Three additional bedrooms each with adjoining full baths

FIRST FLOOR — 1,737 SQ. FT.
SECOND FLOOR — 826 SQ. FT.
BASEMENT — 1,728 SQ. FT.

TOTAL LIVING AREA:
2,563 SQ. FT.

A Karl Kreeger Design

No. 20144

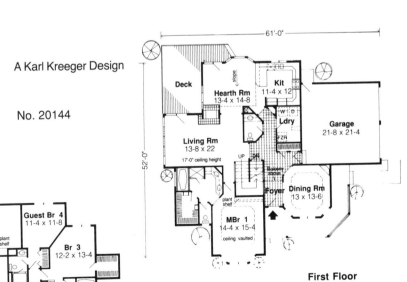

First Floor

Second Floor

No. 10678

Entry Hints At Appealing Interior

■ This plan features:

— Three bedrooms

— Two and one half baths

■ A Family Room with a fireplace opening to a convenient Kitchen with built-in desk, pantry and near-by Laundry area

■ A Dining Room surrounded by a deck and open to the Living Room with vaulted ceilings.

■ A Den and deck upstairs and a Study downstairs

FIRST FLOOR — 1,375 SQ. FT.
SECOND FLOOR — 1,206 SQ. FT.
BASEMENT — 1,375 SQ. FT.

TOTAL LIVING AREA:
2,581 SQ. FT.

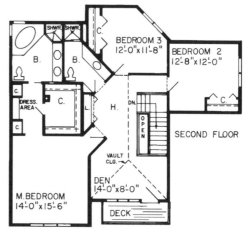

No. 10678

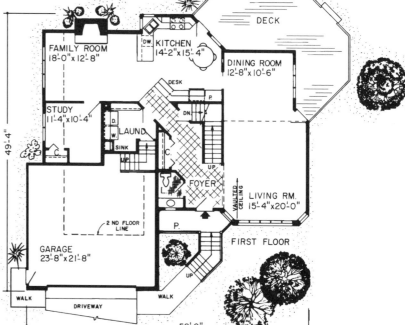

No. 10436
Large Covered Patio for Outdoor Enjoyment

■ This plan features:

— Four bedrooms

— Two full and two half baths

■ A double entry set off by brick-work arches

■ A Family Room and fireplaced Living Room sharing a bar

■ A spacious Master Bedroom including a massive fireplace

■ Three additional bedrooms situated on the second floor

FIRST FLOOR — 2,277 SQ. FT.
SECOND FLOOR — 851 SQ. FT.
GARAGE — 493 SQ. FT.

TOTAL LIVING AREA: 3,128 SQ. FT.

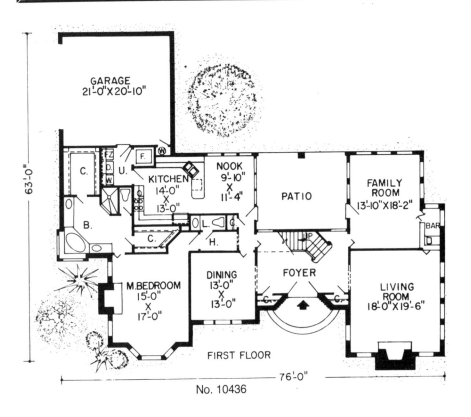

FIRST FLOOR

No. 10436

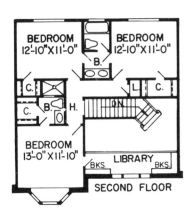

SECOND FLOOR

No. 10679
Dine On The Deck

■ This plan features:

— Three bedrooms

— Two and one half baths

■ A rear-facing Master Suite with his and hers walk-in closets and a luxurious bath overlooking the deck

■ A sunken Living Room with expansive stacked windows and sloping ceilings

■ A range-top island Kitchen open to the Dining area

■ A Sewing Room, Laundry Room and large Garage

FIRST FLOOR — 1,445 SQ. FT.
SECOND FLOOR — 739 SQ. FT.
BASEMENT — 1,229 SQ. FT.
GARAGE — 724 SQ. FT.

TOTAL LIVING AREA:
2,184 SQ. FT.

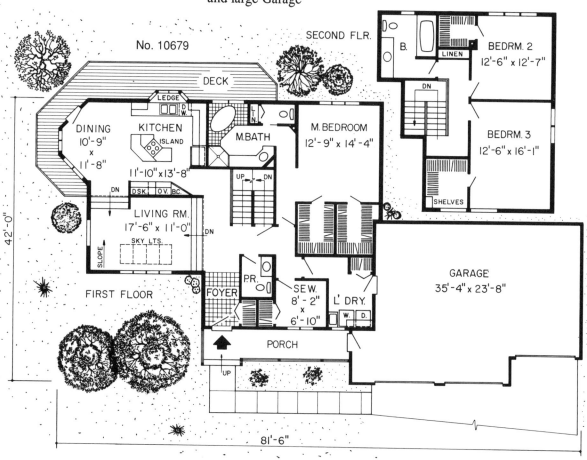

No. 10638

Traditional Warmth With a Modern Accent

■ This plan features

— Four bedrooms

— Two and one half baths

■ Recessed ceilings in the Living Room, Dining and Master Bedrooms

■ Rustic beams, a fireplace and built-in shelves located in the Family Room

■ A laundry room close by the Kitchen with it's cozy breakfast area

■ A Master Suite complete with private bath and bay window sitting nook

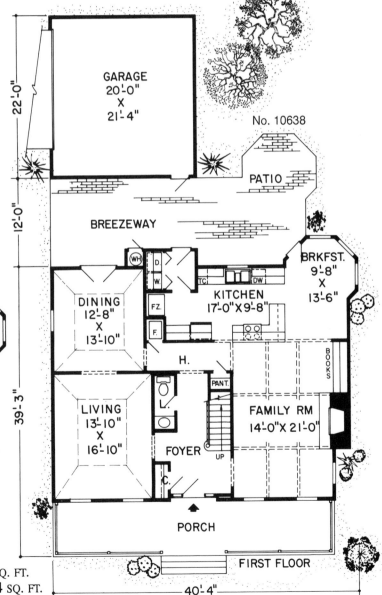

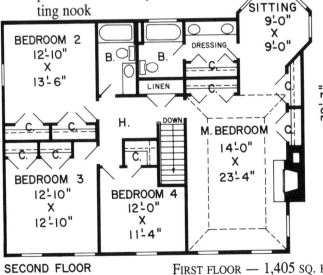

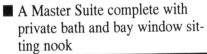

SECOND FLOOR

FIRST FLOOR — 1,405 SQ. FT.

SECOND FLOOR — 1,364 SQ. FT.

GARAGE — 458 SQ. FT.

TOTAL LIVING AREA:

2,769 SQ. FT.

No. 24324
Focus on the Family

■ This plan features:

— Three bedrooms

— Two full and one half baths

■ Cozy front porch

■ A fireplaced Family Room only divided from the Kitchen by an eating bar

■ A U-shaped Kitchen with a pantry and ample cabinet space

■ A pan-vaulted ceiling in the formal Dining Room adds a decorative accent

■ A spacious Living Room, flowing easily into the Dining Room and viewing the front porch

■ A Master Suite enhanced with a walk-in closet, a double vanity, a whirlpool tub, a step-in shower and a compartmentalized toilet

■ Two additional bedrooms, one with a walk-in closet, share the second full bath

FIRST FLOOR — 916 SQ. FT.
SECOND FLOOR — 884 SQ. FT.
GARAGE — 480 SQ. FT.

TOTAL LIVING AREA:
1,800 SQ. FT.

A Don Marshall Design

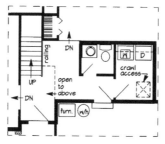

Alternate Crawl Option

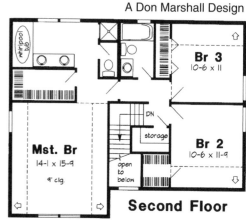

Second Floor

First Floor

No. 24324

No materials list available

24

A Karl Kreeger Design

No. 20071
Traditional Energy Saver

■ This plan features:

— Four bedrooms

— Three and one half baths

■ A heat storing floor in the sun room adjoining the Living Room and Breakfast Room

■ A Living Room with French doors and a massive fireplace

■ A balcony overlooking the soaring two-story foyer and Living Room

■ An island Kitchen centrally-located between the formal and informal Dining Rooms

FIRST FLOOR — 2,186 SQ. FT.
SECOND FLOOR — 983 SQ. FT.
BASEMENT — 2,186 SQ. FT.
GARAGE — 704 SQ. FT.

TOTAL LIVING AREA:
3,169 SQ. FT.

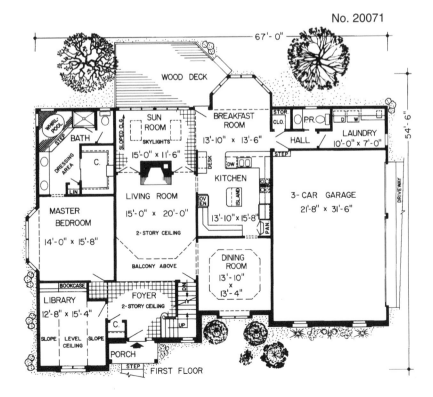

No. 24550

Impressive Brick

■ This plan features:

— Four bedrooms

— Two full and one half bath

■ Decorative facade of brick and windows, and a covered entrance leading into a two-story, raised Foyer with a splendid, curved staircase

■ A Family Room with the unique fireplace and built-in entertainment center opens to the Breakfast/Kitchen area

■ An efficient, island Kitchen with an atrium sink, walk-in pantry, built-in desk expanding to bright Breakfast area and outdoors as well as Utility room and Garage

■ A Master Suite with a vaulted ceiling, over-sized walk-in closet, and a plush Bath with a corner window tub, two vanities and an oversized shower

■ Three additional bedrooms, on second floor, sharing a full bath

FIRST FLOOR — 1,433 SQ. FT.
SECOND FLOOR — 1,283 SQ. FT.
BASEMENT — 1.433 SQ. FT.
GARAGE — 923 SQ. FT.

TOTAL LIVING AREA:
2,716 SQ. FT.

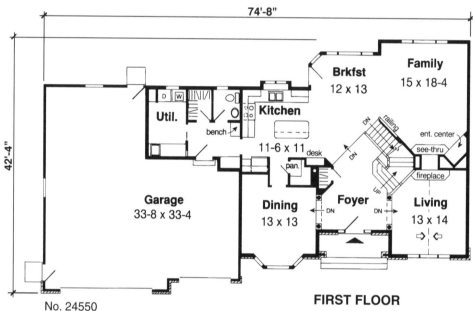

74'-8"

42'-4"

No. 24550

Util.

bench

Garage
33-8 x 33-4

D | W

Kitchen

11-6 x 11 desk

pan.

Brkfst
12 x 13

Family
15 x 18-4

railing

DN

DN

ent. center

see-thru

fireplace

UP

Dining
13 x 13

DN

Foyer

DN

Living
13 x 14

FIRST FLOOR

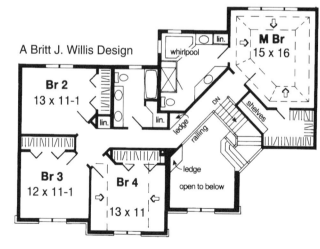

A Britt J. Willis Design

lin.

whirlpool

lin.

M Br
15 x 16

Br 2
13 x 11-1

lin.

lin.

ledge

DN

shelves

railing

Br 3
12 x 11-1

Br 4
13 x 11

ledge

open to below

SECOND FLOOR

No. 20220

Traditional Ranch

■ This plan features:

— Three bedrooms

— Two full baths

■ A large front palladium window that gives this home great curb appeal, and allows a view of the front yard from the Living Room

■ A vaulted ceiling in the Living Room, adding to the architectural interest and the spacious feel of the room

■ Sliding glass doors in the Dining Room that lead to a wood deck

■ A built-in pantry, double sink and breakfast bar in the efficient Kitchen

■ A Master Suite that includes a walk-in closet and a private bath with a double vanity

■ Two additional bedrooms that share a full hall bath

MAIN AREA —1,568 SQ. FT.
BASEMENT — 1,568 SQ. FT.
GARAGE — 509 SQ. FT.

TOTAL LIVING AREA:
1,568 SQ. FT.

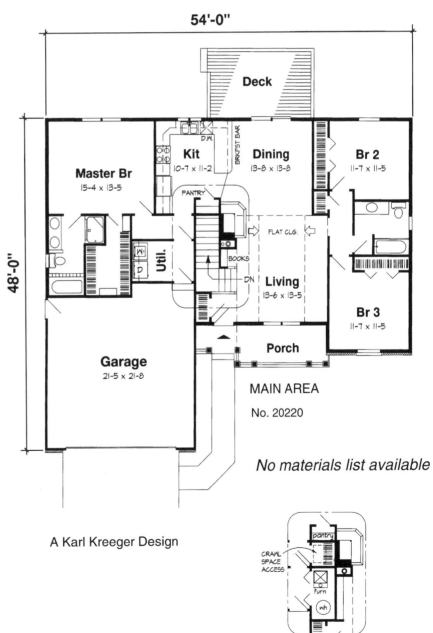

MAIN AREA

No. 20220

No materials list available

A Karl Kreeger Design

No. 20134

Classic Beauty

■ This plan features:

— Three bedrooms

— Two and one half baths

■ Generous, well-placed windows and angular ceilings giving every room a cheery atmosphere

■ The Living and Dining Rooms flowing together off the foyer

■ Family areas at the rear of the home including a cozy Hearth Room adjoining the efficient Kitchen

■ A Master Suite located over the Garage, enhanced by a sky-lit bath, cozy sitting area, and a room-size closet

FIRST FLOOR — 1,361 SQ. FT.
SECOND FLOOR — 1,122 SQ. FT.
BASEMENT — 1,361 SQ. FT.
GARAGE — 477 SQ. FT.

**TOTAL LIVING AREA:
2,483 SQ. FT.**

A Karl Kreeger Design

Second Floor   No. 20134

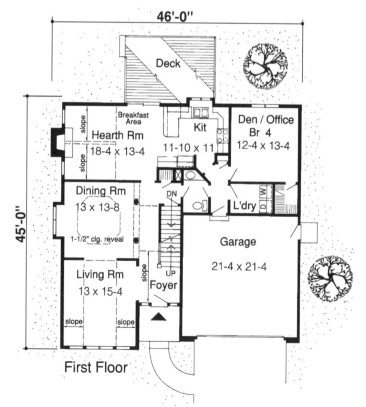

First Floor

No. 10779

Fireplaces Add Warmth

■ This plan features:

— Three bedrooms

— Three full and one half bath

■ A balcony giving a sweeping view of the vaulted Great Room, the two-story foyer, and the bi-level Master Suite

■ A sunken formal Dining Room

■ A country Kitchen with a cook top island and a greenhouse window for growing herbs

■ A book-lined Study next to the Living Room

■ A Master Suite with ample closet space, double vanities, and a large fireplace

FIRST FLOOR — 2,962 SQ. FT.
SECOND FLOOR — 1,883 SQ. FT.
LOWER FLOOR (NOT SHOWN) — 1,888 SQ. FT.
BASEMENT — 1,074 SQ. FT.
GARAGE — 890 SQ. FT.

TOTAL LIVING AREA: 6,733 SQ. FT.

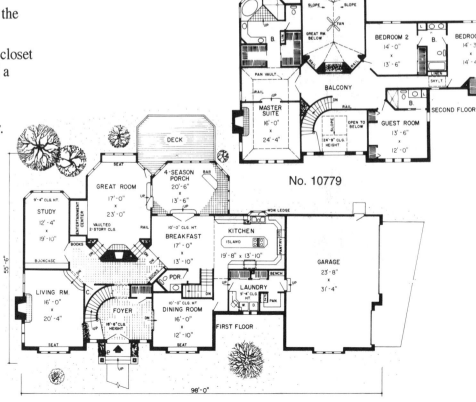

No. 10779

No. 24301
From Times Gone By

■ This plan features:

— Four bedrooms

— Two and one half baths

■ A Family Room opening to a large deck in rear

■ A Master Bedroom with a private bath and ample closet space

■ A large Living Room with a bay window

■ A modern Kitchen with many amenities

FIRST FLOOR — 987 SQ. FT.
SECOND FLOOR — 970 SQ. FT.
BASEMENT — 985 SQ. FT.

TOTAL LIVING AREA:
1,957 SQ. FT.

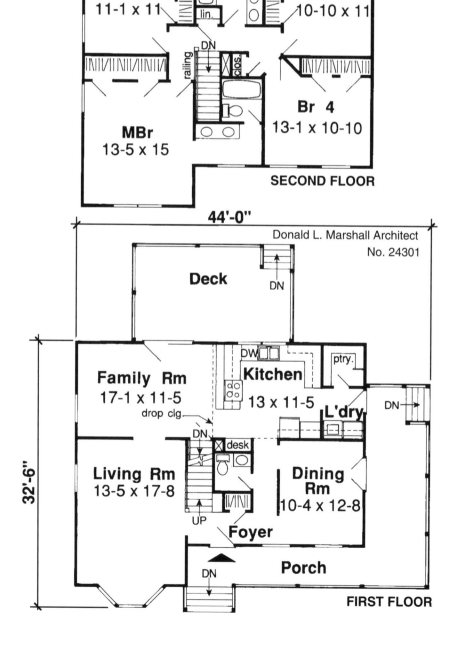

No. 20363

Comfort and Convenience

■ This plan features:

— Three bedrooms

— Two and one half baths

■ Transom windows, skylights, and an open plan combining to make this brick classic a sun-filled retreat

■ Soaring ceilings in the foyer

■ A Family Room including a fireplace and open access to the Kitchen and Breakfast area

■ An island Kitchen with a built-in bar to make mealtime preparation a breeze

■ A luxurious Master Suite with a vaulted bath area including a garden spa

■ Two good-size bedrooms on the second floor, sharing a full bath

FIRST FLOOR — 1,859 SQ. FT.
SECOND FLOOR — 579 SQ. FT.
BASEMENT — 1,859 SQ. FT.
GARAGE — 622 SQ. FT.

TOTAL LIVING AREA:
2,438 SQ. FT.

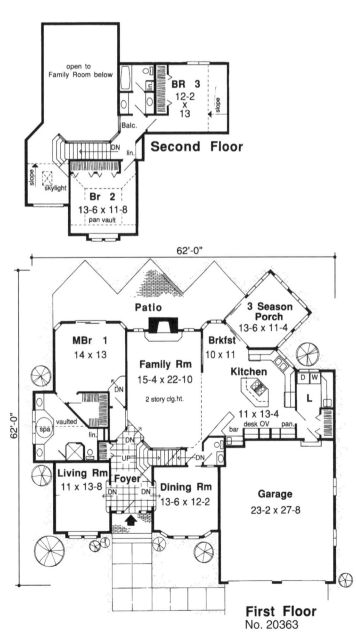

No. 1074
Design Features Six Sides

■ This plan features:

— Three bedrooms

— Two full baths

■ Active living areas centrally located between two quiet bedroom and bath areas

■ A Living Room that can be closed off from bedroom wings giving privacy to both areas

■ A bath located behind a third bedroom

■ A bedroom complete with washer/dryer facilities.

FIRST FLOOR — 1,040 SQ. FT.
STORAGE — 44 SQ. FT.
DECK — 258 SQ. FT.
CARPORT — 230 SQ. FT.

TOTAL LIVING AREA:
1,040 SQ. FT.

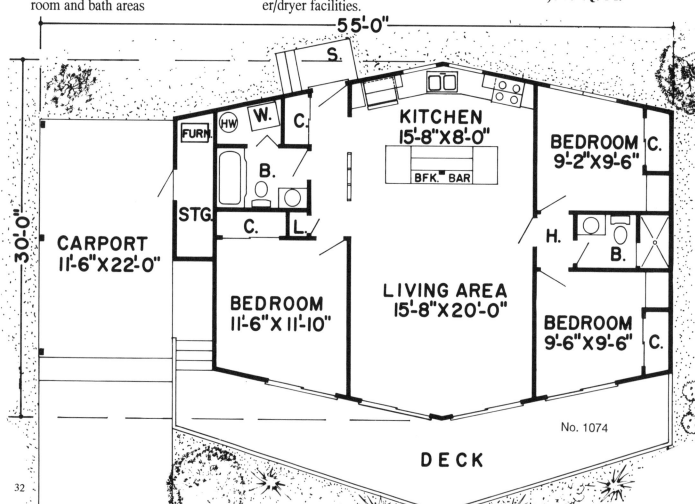

No. 24554
Traditional Interior

■ This plan features:

— Four bedrooms

— Three full and one half baths

■ An appealing symmetrical facade providing a sheltered entrance into open, contemporary living spaces

■ A unique railing defining formal Living Room space with double doors leading to the Family Room

■ A Family Room with a cozy fireplace and triple window view of backyard opens to Kitchen area

■ An ideally located Kitchen with a center work island adjoins the Breakfast bay, formal Dining Room, laundry area, and Garage

■ A comfortable Master Suite with a vaulted ceiling includes a walk-in closet, a private Bath with an oval, window tub, double vanity and separate shower

■ Three additional bedrooms with oversized closets, sharing a full hall bath

FIRST FLOOR — 1,063 SQ. FT.
SECOND FLOOR — 979 SQ. FT.

TOTAL LIVING AREA: 2,042 SQ. FT.

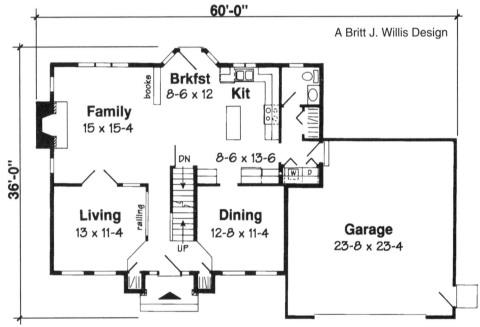

60'-0"

A Britt J. Willis Design

36'-0"

Brkfst 8-6 x 12   **Kit**

books

Family 15 x 15-4

8-6 x 13-6

DN

Living 13 x 11-4

railing

Dining 12-8 x 11-4

W D

UP

Garage 23-8 x 23-4

First Floor

No. 24554

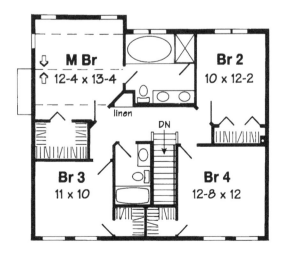

↓ **M Br**
↑ 12-4 x 13-4

Br 2 10 x 12-2

linen

DN

Br 3 11 x 10

Br 4 12-8 x 12

Second Floor

No. 10455
Compact Home Design

■ This plan features:

— Three bedrooms

— Two full baths

■ An airlock Entry which saves energy

■ A Living Room with a window wall, fireplace, built-in bookcases, and a wetbar

■ A step-saver Kitchen with an abundance of storage space and a convenient peninsula

■ A Master Bedroom with separate vanities and walk-in closets

FIRST FLOOR — 1,643 SQ. FT.
GARAGE — 500 SQ. FT.

TOTAL LIVING AREA:
1,643 SQ. FT.

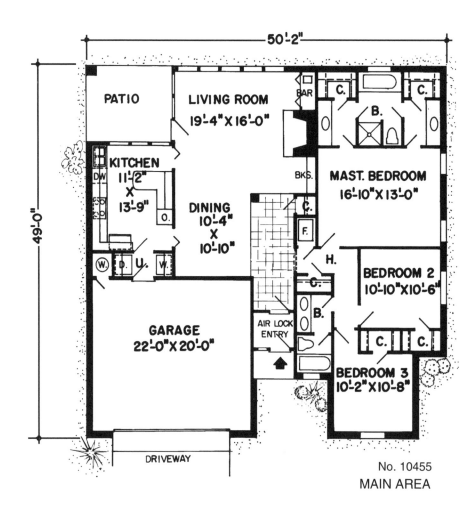

No. 10455
MAIN AREA

No. 20209
Zoned for Harmony

■ This plan features:

— Three bedrooms

— Two and one half baths

■ A lofty vaulted ceiling over the entire living level

■ A spacious, efficient Kitchen with a peninsula counter separating it from the Breakfast Room

■ A formal Living and Dining Room that efficiently flow into each other for ease in entertaining

■ A Family Room with a fireplace and built-in bookshelves

■ A Master Suite with a romantic window seat, a large walk-in closet and a lavish Master Bath

■ Two additional bedrooms, with walk-in closets, that share a full hall bath

FIRST FLOOR — 1,861 SQ. FT.
LOWER FLOOR — 526 SQ. FT.
BASEMENT — 874 SQ. FT.
GARAGE — 574 SQ. FT.

TOTAL LIVING AREA:
2,387 SQ. FT.

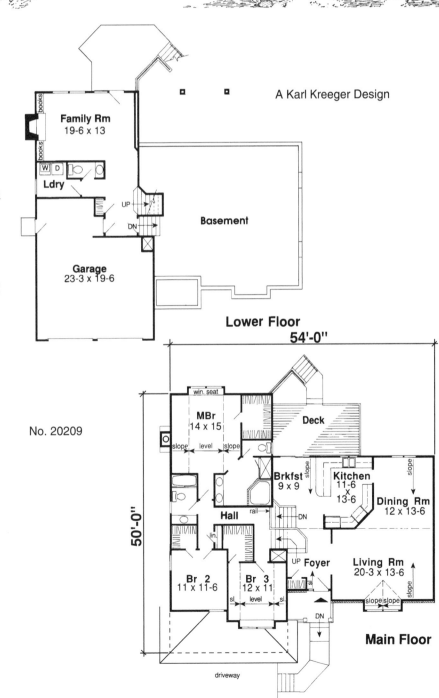

No. 20209

No. 34027

Enticing Two-Story Traditional

■ This plan features:

— Four bedrooms

— Two and one half baths

■ A porch serving as a wonderful, relaxing area to enjoy the outdoors

■ A Dining Room including a decorative ceiling and easy access to the Kitchen

■ A Kitchen/Utility area with access to the Garage

■ A Living Room with double doors into the Family Room which features a fireplace and access to the patio

■ A Master Bedroom with two enormous walk-in closets, as well as a dressing area and private bath

FIRST FLOOR — 925 SQ. FT.
SECOND FLOOR — 975 SQ. FT.
GARAGE — 484 SQ. FT.

No. 34027

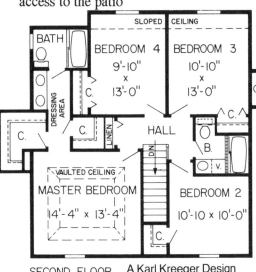

BATH

BEDROOM 4
9'-10"
x
13'-0"

BEDROOM 3
10'-10"
x
13'-0"

SLOPED CEILING

DRESSING AREA

C.

LINEN

HALL

C.

DN

B.

C.

V.

VAULTED CEILING

MASTER BEDROOM
14'-4" x 13'-4"

BEDROOM 2
10'-10 x 10'-0"

C.

SECOND FLOOR   A Karl Kreeger Design

**TOTAL LIVING AREA:
1,900 SQ. FT.**

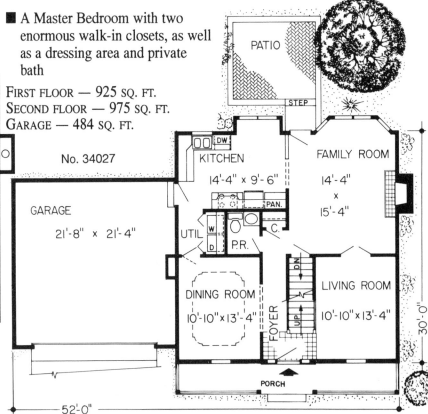

PATIO

STEP

KITCHEN
14'-4" x 9'-6"

FAMILY ROOM
14'-4"
x
15'-4"

DW

PAN.

UTIL
W
D

P.R.

C.

GARAGE
21'-8" x 21'-4"

DINING ROOM
10'-10"x13'-4"

FOYER

UP

DN

LIVING ROOM
10'-10"x13'-4"

PORCH

52'-0"

30'-0"

No. 20195

Cozy and Restful

■ This plan features:

— Three bedrooms

— One and one half baths

■ A decorative ceiling in the Master Bedroom with private access to the full hall sky-lit bath

■ A convenient laundry center near the bedrooms

■ An efficient Kitchen with ample counter and cabinet space and a double sink under a window

■ A Dining/Living Room combination that flows into each other for easy entertaining

■ A Family Room with a cozy fireplace and convenient half bath

FIRST FLOOR — 1,139 SQ. FT.
BASEMENT — 288 SQ. FT.
GARAGE — 598 SQ. FT.

TOTAL LIVING AREA:
1,427 SQ. FT.

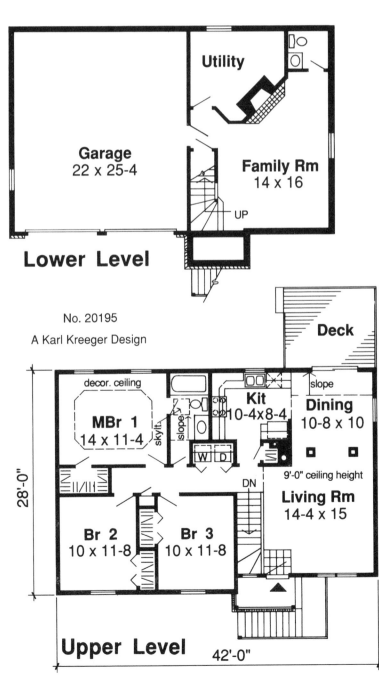

No. 20195

A Karl Kreeger Design

Lower Level

Utility

Garage
22 x 25-4

Family Rm
14 x 16

UP

Upper Level

Deck

decor. ceiling

MBr 1
14 x 11-4

Kit
10-4x8-4

Dining
10-8 x 10

skylt.
slope

slope

W D

DN

9'-0" ceiling height

Living Rm
14-4 x 15

Br 2
10 x 11-8

Br 3
10 x 11-8

28'-0"

42'-0"

No. 20083

One-Level with a Twist

■ This plan features:

— Three bedrooms

— Two full baths

■ Wide-open active areas that are centrally located

■ A spacious Dining, Living, and Kitchen area

■ A Master Suite at the rear of the house with a full bath

■ Two additional bedrooms that share a full hall bath and the quiet atmosphere that results from an intelligent design

FIRST FLOOR — 1,575 SQ. FT.
BASEMENT —1,575 SQ. FT.
GARAGE —475 SQ. FT.

TOTAL LIVING AREA:
1,575 SQ. FT.

A Karl Kreeger Design

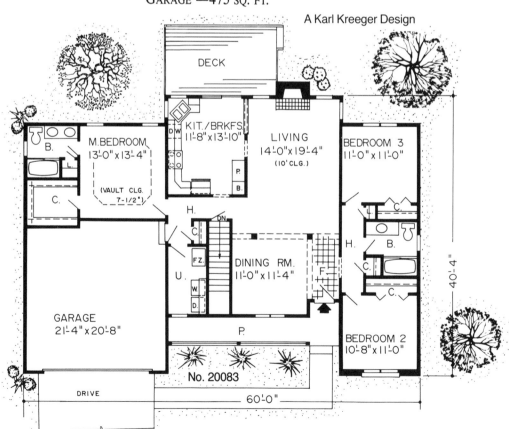

No. 20198

Dramatic Ranch

■ This plan features:

— Three bedrooms

— Two full baths

■ A large Living Room with a stone fireplace and decorative beamed ceiling

■ A Kitchen/Dining Room arrangement which makes the rooms seem more spacious

■ A Laundry with large pantry located close to the bedrooms and the Kitchen

■ A Master Bedroom with walk-in closet and private Master Bath

■ Two additional bedrooms, one with a walk-in closet, that share the full hall bath

FIRST FLOOR — 1,792 SQ. FT.
BASEMENT — 864 SQ. FT.
GARAGE — 928 SQ. FT.

TOTAL LIVING AREA: 1,792 SQ. FT.

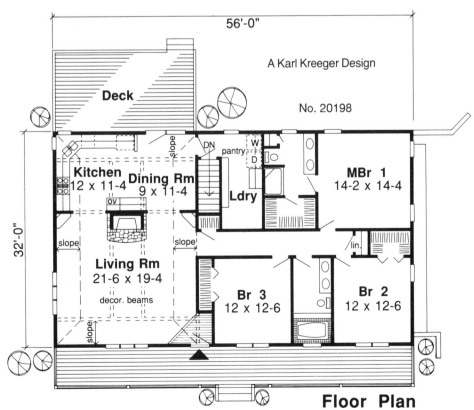

56'-0"

A Karl Kreeger Design

No. 20198

Deck

32'-0"

Kitchen 12 x 11-4

Dining Rm 9 x 11-4

pantry

W D

Ldry

MBr 1 14-2 x 14-4

slope

slope

slope

Living Rm 21-6 x 19-4

decor. beams

lin.

Br 3 12 x 12-6

Br 2 12 x 12-6

DN

ov

Floor Plan

No. 20080
Window Graces Parlor

■ This plan features:

— Three bedrooms

— Two and one half baths

■ A brick and stucco facade with rustic wood trim

■ A Family Room with a massive fireplace and ten-foot ceilings

■ An island Kitchen and Breakfast Nook adjacent to a gracious formal Dining Room

■ A first floor Master Suite with a private bath and an abundance of closet space

FIRST FLOOR — 1,859 SQ. FT.
SECOND FLOOR — 556 SQ. FT.
BASEMENT — 1,844 SQ. FT.
GARAGE — 598 SQ. FT.

TOTAL LIVING AREA:
2,415 SQ. FT.

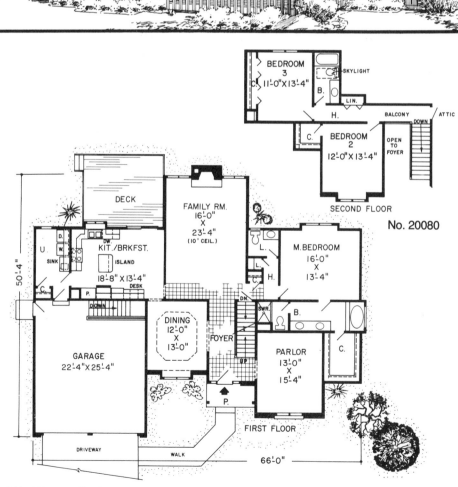

A Karl Kreeger Design

No. 24309

Rustic Retreat

■ This plan features:

— Two bedrooms

— One full bath

■ A wrap-around deck equipped with a built-in bar-b-que for easy outdoor living

■ An entry, in a wall of glass opens the Living area to the outdoors

■ A large fireplace in the Living area opens into an efficient Kitchen, with a built-in pantry, that serves the Nook area

■ Two bedrooms share a centrally-located full bath with a window tub

■ A loft area ready for multiple uses

MAIN FLOOR — 897 SQ. FT.

MAIN LIVING AREA:
897 SQ. FT.

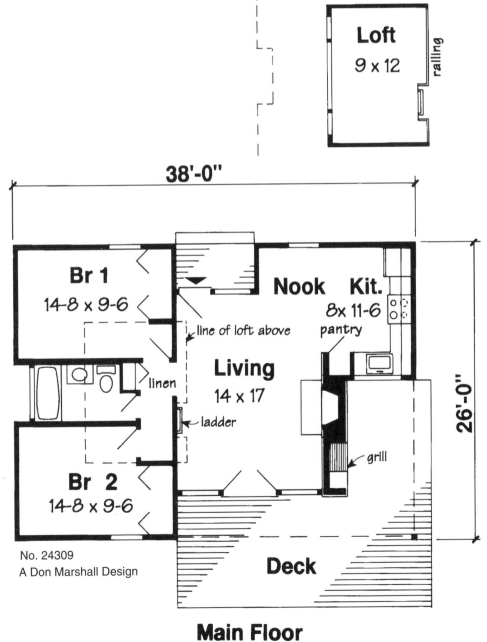

Loft
9 x 12

railing

38'-0"

26'-0"

Br 1
14-8 x 9-6

Nook   **Kit.**
8 x 11-6

line of loft above

pantry

linen

Living
14 x 17

ladder

Br 2
14-8 x 9-6

grill

No. 24309
A Don Marshall Design

Deck

Main Floor

No. 20143
Stunning Split Entry

■ This plan features:

— Three bedrooms

— Two full baths

■ A Recreation Room with built-in bar, powder room, and storage space

■ A Master suite featuring a walk-in closet, double vanitied bath, and decorative ceilings

■ The Dining Room also features decorative ceilings and columns

UPPER FLOOR — 1,599 SQ. FT.
LOWER FLOOR — 346 SQ. FT.
GARAGE — 520 SQ. FT.

TOTAL LIVING AREA: 1,945 SQ. FT.

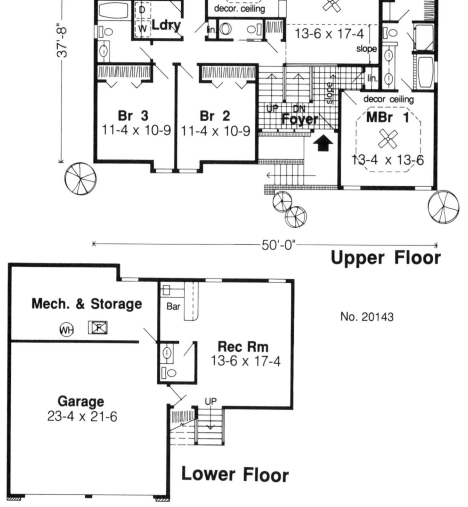

A Karl Kreeger Design

Deck

Brkfst 7-6 x 8-6

Kitchen 9 x 10-4   skylt.

pan. desk

Dining Rm 10-6 x 11
decor. ceiling

Living Rm
slope

13-6 x 17-4
slope

Ldry
lin.

37'-8"

Br 3 11-4 x 10-9

Br 2 11-4 x 10-9

UP DN **Foyer**

decor ceiling

lin.

MBr 1 13-4 x 13-6

50'-0"

Upper Floor

Mech. & Storage
WH

Bar

No. 20143

Rec Rm 13-6 x 17-4

Garage 23-4 x 21-6

UP

Lower Floor

No. 20196

Gorgeous and Livable

■ This plan features:

— Four bedrooms

— Three full baths

■ A bay window that enhances the Living Room with natural light

■ A decorative ceiling accentuating the formal Dining Room

■ A Breakfast room with an incredible shape

■ An island Kitchen with an efficient layout and in close proximity to both the formal Dining Room and the informal Breakfast Room

■ A spacious Family Room that is warmed by a cozy fireplace

■ A fantastic Master Suite with a decorative ceiling, private Master Bath and a large walk-in closet

■ Three additional bedrooms with walk-in closets, that share a full hall bath

FIRST FLOOR — 1,273 SQ. FT.
SECOND FLOOR — 1,477 SQ. FT.
BASEMENT — 974 SQ. FT.
GARAGE — 852 SQ. FT.

TOTAL LIVING AREA:
2,750 SQ. FT.

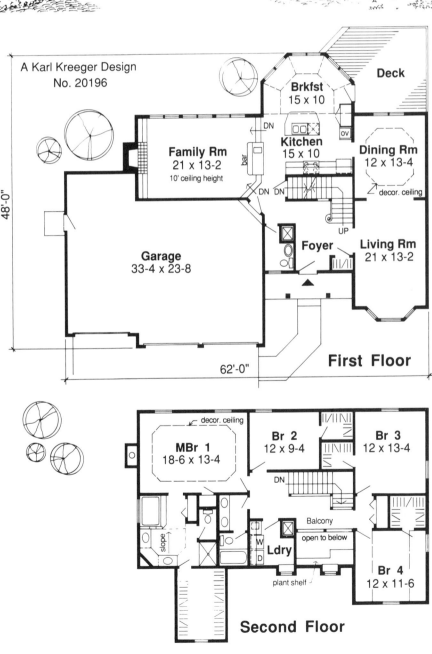

A Karl Kreeger Design
No. 20196

Deck

Brkfst 15 x 10

Kitchen 15 x 10

Family Rm 21 x 13-2
10' ceiling height

Dining Rm 12 x 13-4
decor. ceiling

DN

bar

DN DN

UP

Garage 33-4 x 23-8

Foyer

Living Rm 21 x 13-2

48'-0"

62'-0"

First Floor

decor. ceiling

MBr 1 18-6 x 13-4

Br 2 12 x 9-4

Br 3 12 x 13-4

DN

slope

Ldry
W
D

Balcony
open to below

plant shelf

Br 4 12 x 11-6

Second Floor

No. 10515

Open Plan Accented By Loft, Windows and Decks

■ This plan features:

— Three bedrooms

— Two and one half baths

■ A fireplaced Family Room

■ A fireplaced Dining Room

■ A large Kitchen sharing a preparation/eating bar with Dining Room

■ A first floor Master Bedroom featuring two closets and a five-piece bath

■ An ample Utility Room designed with a pantry and room for a freezer, a washer and dryer, plus a furnace and a hot water heater

FIRST FLOOR — 1,280 SQ. FT.
SECOND FLOOR — 735 SQ. FT.
GREENHOUSE — 80 SQ. FT.

TOTAL LIVING AREA: 2,015 SQ. FT.

No. 10515

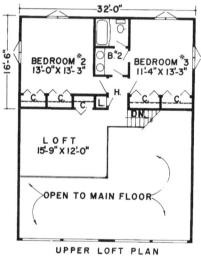

UPPER LOFT PLAN

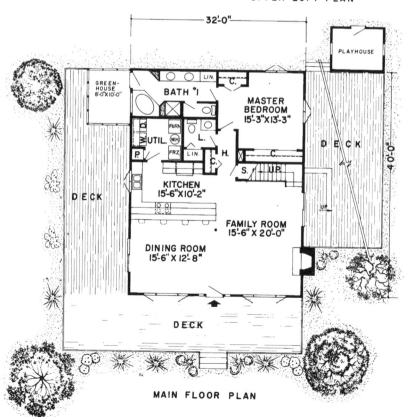

MAIN FLOOR PLAN

No. 34055

Ranch Provides Great Floor Plan

■ This plan features:

— Four bedrooms

— Two full baths

■ A large Living Room and Dining Room flowing together into one open space perfect for entertaining

■ A Laundry area, which doubles as a mud room, off the Kitchen

■ A Master Suite including a private bath

■ A two-car Garage

FIRST FLOOR — 1,527 SQ. FT.
BASEMENT — 1,344 SQ. FT.
GARAGE — 425 SQ. FT.

TOTAL LIVING AREA:
1,527 SQ. FT.

Dining
11-6 x 13-6

pantry

Br 4
12 x 11-2

Alternate Plan
w/ Crawlspace

70'-0"

28'-0"

Ldry
W D

Kit 12-4 x 8

Dining Rm
11 x 13-6

pantry

Br 4
11-8 x 11-2

MBr 1
12 x 13-6

Garage
22 x 20

DN

linen

Living Rm
20-4 x 13-6

Br 3
12 x 10

Br 2
12 x 11-2

No. 34055

No. 24263

Family Home with all the Amenities

■ This plan features:

— Four bedrooms

— Two full and one half bath

■ A see-through fireplace between the Living Room and the Family Room

■ A gourmet Kitchen with an island, built-in pantry and double sink

■ A Master Bedroom with a vaulted ceiling

■ A Master Bath with large double vanity, linen closet, corner tub, separate shower, compartmented toilet, and huge walk-in closet

■ Three additional bedrooms, one with a walk-in closet, share a full hall Bath

FIRST FLOOR — 1,241 SQ. FT.
SECOND FLOOR — 1,170 SQ. FT.

TOTAL LIVING AREA: 2,411 SQ. FT.

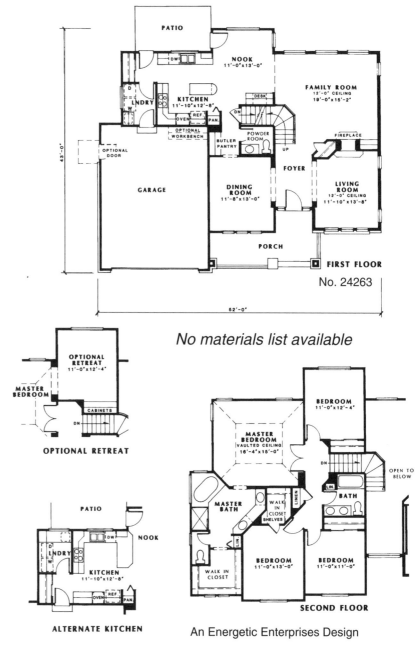

No materials list available

An Energetic Enterprises Design

No. 10663

Perfect for Parties

■ This plan features:

— Three bedrooms

— Three and one half baths

■ Two bedroom suites with two full baths adjoining a sitting room on the second floor

■ A vaulted Family Room with fireplace and a bay window in the Living Room

■ An elegant Dining Room with floor-to-ceiling windows and Study nearby

■ A Nook nestled between the Kitchen and the utility room

FIRST FLOOR — 2,310 SQ. FT.
SECOND FLOOR — 866 SQ. FT.
GARAGE — 679 SQ. FT.

**TOTAL LIVING AREA:
3,176 SQ. FT.**

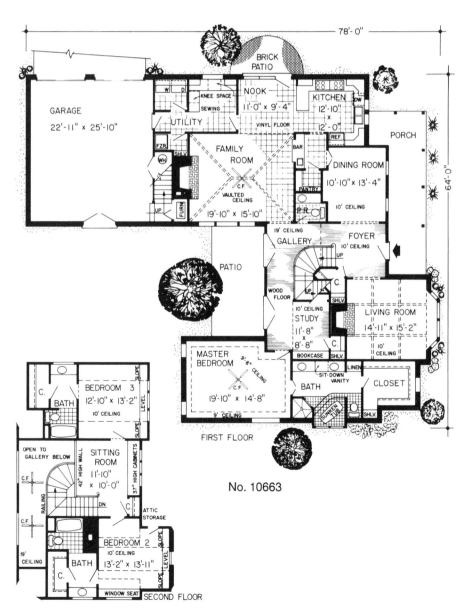

No. 10663

No. 20160

Streetside Appeal

■ This plan features:

— Three bedrooms

— Two full and one half baths

■ An elegant Living and Dining Room combination that is divided by columns

■ A Family/Hearth Room with a two-way fireplace to the Breakfast room

■ A well-appointed Kitchen with built-in pantry, peninsula counter and double corner sink

■ A Master Suite with decorative ceiling, walk-in closet and private bath

■ Two additional bedrooms that share a full hall bath

FIRST FLOOR — 1,590 SQ. FT.
SECOND FLOOR — 567 SQ. FT.
BASEMENT — 1,576 SQ. FT.
GARAGE — 456 SQ. FT.

TOTAL LIVING AREA:
2,157 SQ. FT.

A Karl Kreeger Design

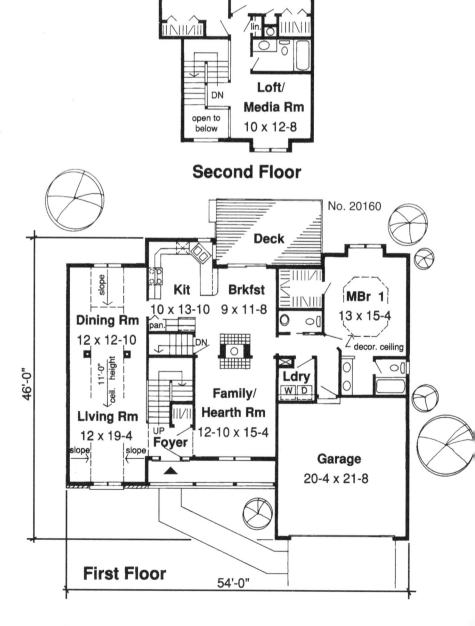

Br 3
10-4 x 11

Br 2
12-8 x 10

lin.

Loft/ Media Rm
10 x 12-8

DN

open to below

Second Floor

No. 20160

Deck

Kit
10 x 13-10

Brkfst
9 x 11-8

MBr 1
13 x 15-4

decor. ceiling

Dining Rm
12 x 12-10

pan.

DN

Ldry
W D

46'-0"

11'-0" ceil. height

slope

Living Rm
12 x 19-4

UP

Foyer

Family/ Hearth Rm
12-10 x 15-4

Garage
20-4 x 21-8

slope slope

First Floor

54'-0"

No. 24700
Fan-lights Highlight Facade

■ This plan features:

— Three bedrooms

— Two full baths

■ Front Porch entry leads into an open Living Room, accented by a hearth fireplace below a sloped ceiling

■ Efficient Kitchen with a peninsula counter convenient to the Laundry, Garage, Dining area and Deck

■ Master Bedroom accented by a decorative ceiling, a double closet and a private bath

■ Two additional bedrooms with decorative windows and ample closets share a full bath

■ This plan is available with a Basement, Slab, or Crawlspace foundation. Please specify when ordering

MAIN FLOOR — 1,312 SQ. FT.
BASEMENT — 1,293 SQ. FT.
GARAGE — 445 SQ. FT.

TOTAL LIVING AREA: 1,312 SQ. FT.

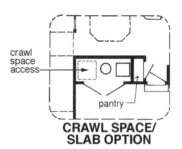

crawl space access

pantry

CRAWL SPACE/ SLAB OPTION

No materials list available

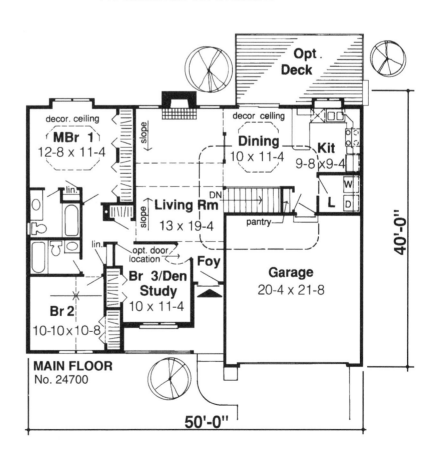

Opt. Deck

decor. ceiling

MBr 1
12-8 x 11-4

slope
↓

decor. ceiling

Dining
10 x 11-4

Kit
9-8 x9-4

lin.

slope

Living Rm
13 x 19-4

DN

pantry

W
L
D

lin.

opt. door location

Foy

Br 3/Den Study
10 x 11-4

Garage
20-4 x 21-8

Br 2
10-10 x 10-8

40'-0"

MAIN FLOOR
No. 24700

50'-0"

No. 20062

Inexpensive Ranch Design

■ This plan features:

— Three bedrooms

— Two full baths

■ A large picture window brightening the Breakfast area

■ A well planned Kitchen

■ A Living Room which is accented by an open beam across the sloping ceiling and wood burning fireplace

■ A Master Bedroom with an extremely large bath area

FIRST FLOOR — 1,500 SQ. FT.
BASEMENT — 1,500 SQ. FT.
GARAGE — 482 SQ. FT.

**TOTAL LIVING AREA:
1,500 SQ. FT.**

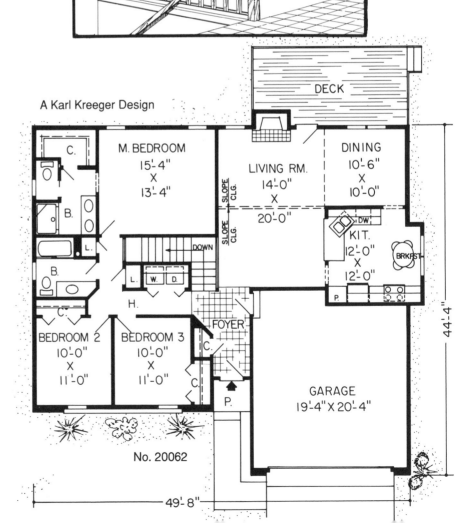

A Karl Kreeger Design

No. 20062

No. 92536

Traditional Brick with Detailing

■ This plan features:

—Three bedrooms

—Two full baths

■ Covered entry leads into the Foyer, the formal Dining Room and the Den

■ Expansive Den with a decorative ceiling over a hearth fireplace and sliding glass doors to the rear yard

■ Country Kitchen with a built-in pantry, double ovens and a cooktop island easily serves the Breakfast area and Dining Room

■ Private Master Bedroom suite with a decorative ceiling, a walk-in closet, a double vanity and a whirlpool tub

■ Two additional bedrooms share a full bath

■ This plan is available with a Slab or Crawlspace foundation. Please specify when ordering

MAIN FLOOR — 1,869 SQ. FT.
GARAGE — 484 SQ. FT.

TOTAL LIVING AREA:
1,869 SQ. FT.

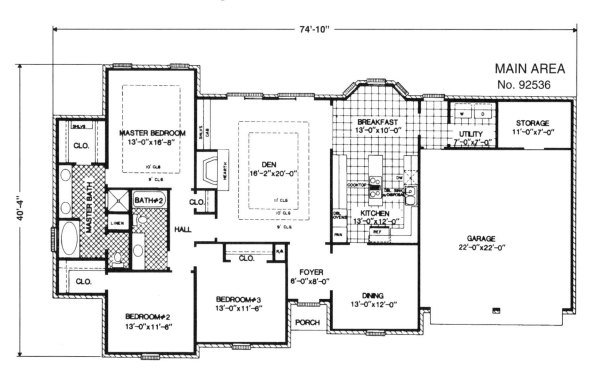

No. 10698

Vaulted Ceilings Make Every Room Special

■ This plan features:

— Five bedrooms

— Four full and one half baths

■ An enjoyable view from the island Kitchen which is separated from the Morning Room by only a counter

■ Access to the pool from the covered patio or from the Living and Family Rooms

■ The Living and Family Rooms with beamed ten-foot ceilings and massive fireplaces

■ A Master Suite with a raised tub, built-in dressing tables and a fireplaced Sitting room with vaulted ceiling

FIRST FLOOR — 4,014 SQ. FT.

SECOND FLOOR — 727 SQ. FT.

GARAGE — 657 SQ. FT.

TOTAL LIVING AREA:
4,741 SQ. FT.

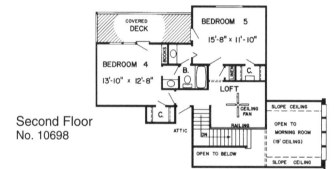

Second Floor
No. 10698

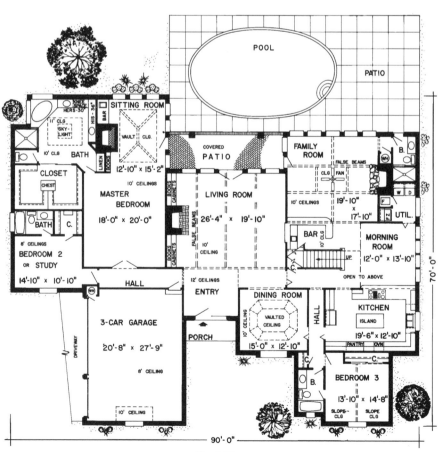

First Floor

No. 10749

A Celebration of Traditional Elements

■ This plan features:

— Four bedrooms

— Two full and two half baths

■ High ceilings with cooling fans and loads of built-in storage

■ Every bedroom adjoining a bath and the Master Suite enjoying access to the outdoor deck

■ A massive fireplace located the roomy Family Room

■ A Kitchen, Breakfast area, Sewing room, Dining Room and pantry all located within steps of each other for convenience

FIRST FLOOR — 3,438 SQ. FT.
GARAGE — 610 SQ. FT.

**TOTAL LIVING AREA:
3,438 SQ. FT.**

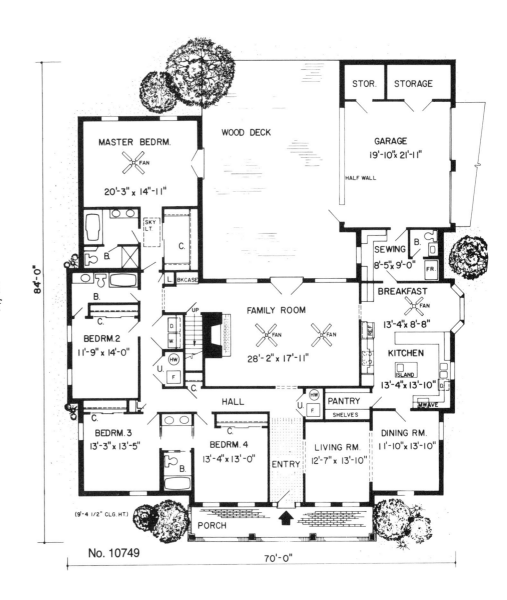

No. 24269

Vaulted Ceiling in the Living Room and the Master Suite

■ This plan features:

— Three or four bedrooms

— Two full and one half baths

■ A vaulted ceiling in the Living Room adding to its spaciousness

■ A formal Dining Room with easy access to both the Living Room and the Kitchen

■ An efficient Kitchen with double sinks, and ample storage and counter space

■ An informal Eating Nook with a built-in pantry

■ A large Family Room with a fireplace

■ A plush Master Suite with a vaulted ceiling and luxurious Master Bath and two walk-in closets

■ Two additional bedrooms share a full bath with a convenient laundry chute

FIRST FLOOR — 1,115 SQ. FT.
SECOND FLOOR — 1,129 SQ. FT.
BASEMENT — 1,096 SQ. FT.
GARAGE — 415 SQ. FT.

TOTAL LIVING AREA:
2,244 SQ. FT.

No materials list available

An Energetic Enterprises Design

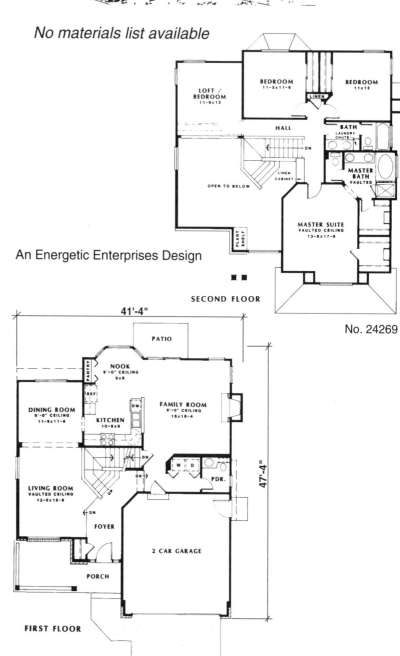

No. 24269

54

No. 26001
Rural Farmhouse Profile

■ This plan features:

— Four bedrooms

— Three full baths

■ A varied gabled roof and large railed front porch, creating a picturesque rural farmhouse

■ Formal living areas, Living Room and Dining Room, are located in the front of the home

■ A Dining Room graced by a bay window and a masonry fireplace

■ A well-appointed, efficient Kitchen, with ample work space and a double sink

■ A double Garage with a sheltered breezeway/porch entrance opening to the Utility Room

■ A first floor Master Suite equipped with a walk-in closet and a private full Bath

■ Three additional bedrooms, one with a walk-in closet, that share a full hall bath

FIRST FLOOR — 1,184 SQ. FT.
SECOND FLOOR — 821 SQ. FT.
BASEMENT — 821 SQ. FT.
GARAGE — 576 SQ. FT.
FRONT PORCH — 176 SQ. FT.
SIDE PORCH — 69 SQ. FT.

TOTAL LIVING AREA:
2,005 SQ. FT.

No. 10396

Three Levels of Living Space

■ This plan features:

—Three bedrooms

— Three baths

■ A passive solar design suitable for vacation or year round living

■ The southern elevation of the home highlighted by an abundance of decks

■ The Basement level including a large shop, storage, and recreation area plus a bedroom

■ An angled wall lending character to the Kitchen/Dining area

■ A Master Bedroom occupying the entire second floor with its own private bath, walk in closet, and storage nook

FIRST FLOOR — 886 SQ. FT.
SECOND FLOOR — 456 SQ. FT.
BASEMENT — 886 SQ. FT.

TOTAL LIVING AREA: 2,228 SQ. FT.

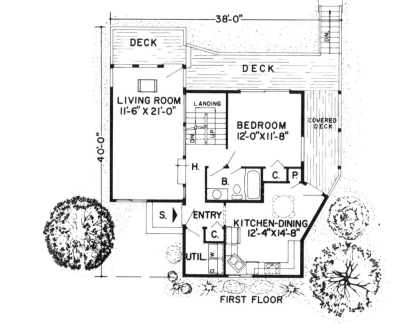

FIRST FLOOR

BASEMENT

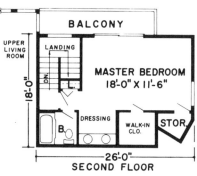

SECOND FLOOR

No. 10396

No. 10673

Bay Windows and Skylights Brighten This Tudor Home

- This plan features:
- — Four bedrooms
- — Two and one half baths
- A Kitchen equipped with a pantry and Breakfast Nook leading onto a brick patio

- An oversized Living Room with skylights and a fireplace
- A Master Suite containing a whirlpool tub

FIRST FLOOR — 1,265 SQ. FT.
SECOND FLOOR — 1,210 SQ. FT.
BASEMENT — 1,247 SQ. FT.
GARAGE — 506 SQ. FT.

TOTAL LIVING AREA:
2,475 SQ. FT.

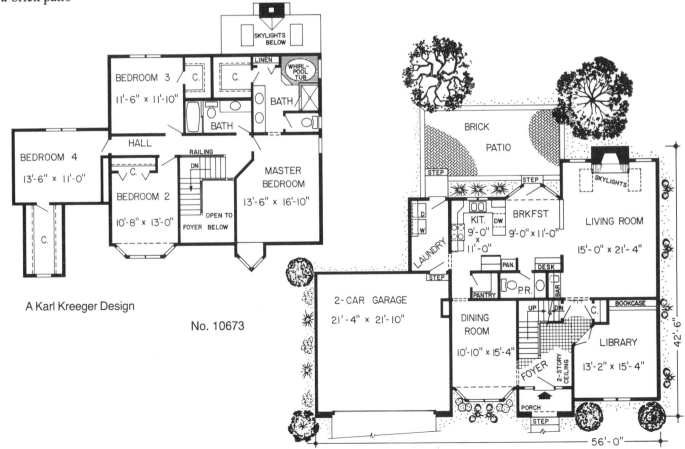

A Karl Kreeger Design

No. 10673

No. 20139
Have it All

■ This plan features:
— Three bedrooms
— Two full baths

■ A classic brick and clapboard exterior adorned with an old-fashioned bay a window

■ An elegant Living Room with a fireplace flowing into a formal Dining Room with sliders to a rear deck

■ A compact Kitchen opening to the Dining Room for a spacious feel

■ A well-appointed Master Suite with ample closet space and a four-piece private bath

FIRST FLOOR — 1,488 SQ. FT.
BASEMENT — 1,488 SQ. FT.
GARAGE — 484 SQ. FT.

TOTAL LIVING AREA:
1,488 SQ. FT.

No. 20139

A Karl Kreeger Design

Deck

Br 3
10 x 10

Dining
11 x 15

Kit
10 x 11-8

MBr 1
13 x 13-4

7-1/2" ceiling reveal

slope

plant shelf above

skylight

lin.

Br 2
12-8 x 10-4

Living Rm
12-10 x 19-6

9'-0" ceiling height

Garage
21-4 x 22-2

DN

W
D

First Floor

42'-0"

54'-0"

No. 10674
Carefree Convenience

■ This plan features:
— Three bedrooms
— Two full baths

■ A galley Kitchen, centrally-located between the Dining, Breakfast and Living Room areas

■ A huge Family Room which exits onto the patio

■ The Master Suite boasts both double closets and double vanities

■ Two additional bedrooms share a full hall bath

MAIN AREA — 1,600 SQ. FT.
GARAGE — 465 SQ. FT.

TOTAL LIVING AREA:
1,600 SQ. FT

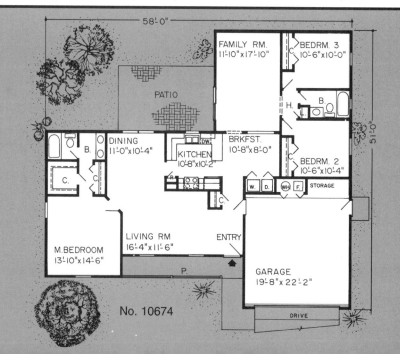

58'-0"

FAMILY RM.
11'-10"x17'-10"

BEDRM. 3
10'-6"x10'-0"

PATIO

B.

DINING
11'-0"x10'-4"

KITCHEN
10'-8"x10'-2"

BRKFST.
10'-8"x8'-0"

BEDRM. 2
10'-6"x10'-4"

W. D. WH F. STORAGE

51'-0"

M. BEDROOM
13'-10"x14'-6"

LIVING RM
16'-4"x11'-6"

ENTRY

GARAGE
19'-8"x 22'-2"

P

DRIVE

No. 10674

No. 10548
Sloped Ceiling Attractive Feature of Ranch Design

■ This plan features:
— Three bedrooms
— Two and one half baths
■ A fireplace and sloped ceiling in the Living Room
■ A Master Bedroom complete with a full bath, shower and dressing area
■ A decorative ceiling in the Dining Room

FIRST FLOOR — 1,688 SQ. FT.
BASEMENT — 1,688 SQ. FT.
SCREENED PORCH — 120 SQ. FT.
GARAGE — 489 SQ. FT.

TOTAL LIVING AREA:
1,688 SQ. FT.

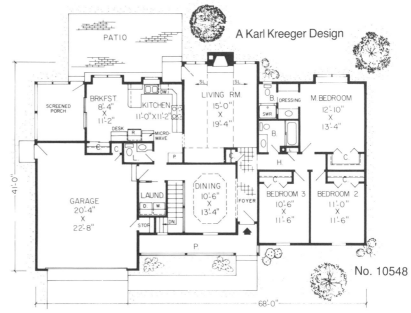

A Karl Kreeger Design

PATIO

SCREENED PORCH

BRKFST. 8'-4" X 11'-2"

KITCHEN 11'-0" X 11'-2"

LIVING RM. 15'-0" X 19'-4"

DRESSING

M. BEDROOM 12'-10" X 13'-4"

GARAGE 20'-4" X 22'-8"

LAUND.

DINING 10'-6" X 13'-4"

FOYER

BEDROOM 3 10'-6" X 11'-6"

BEDROOM 2 11'-0" X 11'-6"

41'-0"

68'-0"

No. 10548

No. 20156
Family Favorite

■ This plan features:
— Three bedrooms
— Two full baths

■ An open arrangement with the Dining Room that combines with ten-foot ceilings to make the Living Room seem more spacious

■ Glass on three sides of the Dining Room overlooking the deck

■ An efficient, compact Kitchen with built-in pantry and peninsula counter

■ A Master Suite with romantic window seat and compartmentalized private bath and walk-in closet

■ Two additional bedrooms that share a full hall closet

FIRST FLOOR — 1,359 SQ. FT.
BASEMENT — 1,359 SQ. FT.
GARAGE — 501 SQ. FT.

TOTAL LIVING AREA:
1,359 SQ. FT.

A Karl Kreeger Design

Deck

Dining
11 x 11-4
decor. ceiling

Br 2
10-10 x 11-10

Den/Br 3
10 x 11-10

Kit
10 x 11-4

W D

Ldr

opt. door location

solid wall w/ opt. door location

DN

pan.

34'-0"

lin.

decor. ceiling

MBr 1
11-8 x 13-4

Living Rm
14-4 x 16-10
10'-0" ceiling height

Garage
20-4 x 21-8

seat

Floor Plan

58'-0"

No. 20156

No. 20161
Delightful Doll House

■ This plan features:
— Three bedrooms
— Two full baths

■ A sloped ceiling in the Living Room which also has a focal point fireplace

■ An efficient Kitchen with peninsula counter and built-in pantry

■ A decorative ceiling and sliding glass doors to the deck in the Dining Room

■ A Master Suite with a decorative ceiling, ample closet space and a private full bath

■ Two additional bedrooms that share a full hall bath

FIRST FLOOR — 1,307 SQ. FT.
BASEMENT — 1,298 SQ. FT.
GARAGE — 462 SQ. FT.

TOTAL LIVING AREA:
1,307 SQ. FT.

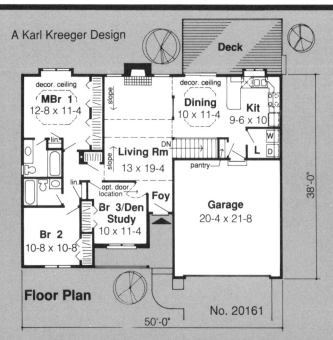

A Karl Kreeger Design

Deck

decor. ceiling

MBr 1
12-8 x 11-4

slope

decor. ceiling

Dining
10 x 11-4

Kit
9-6 x 10

slope

Living Rm
13 x 19-4

DN

W D

L

pantry

lin.

lin.

opt. door location

Foy

Br 3/Den
Study
10 x 11-4

Garage
20-4 x 21-8

38'-0"

Br 2
10-8 x 10-8

Floor Plan

50'-0"

No. 20161

No. 20154
Fabulous Facade

■ This plan features:
— Three Bedrooms
— Two full baths

■ A spacious Living Room with a sloped ceiling and a large fireplace

■ A decorative ceiling and bow window in the Dining Room which has an open floor plan to the Kitchen

■ An efficient and well-appointed Kitchen having a built-in pantry and double sink located under a window

■ An ornamental ceiling in the Master Suite which is equipped with a walk-in closet and sky-lit private bath

■ Two additional bedrooms sharing a full hall bath

FIRST FLOOR — 1,420 SQ. FT.
BASEMENT — 1,392 SQ. FT.
GARAGE — 442 SQ. FT.

TOTAL LIVING AREA:
1,420 SQ. FT.

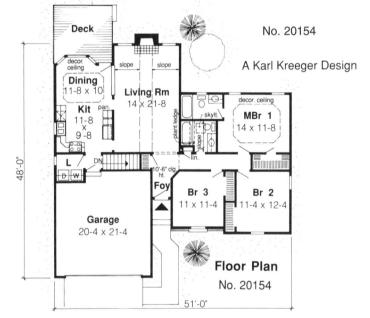

No. 20154

A Karl Kreeger Design

Deck

decor. ceiling

Dining
11-8 x 10

Kit
11-8
X
9 -8

pan.

slope   slope

Living Rm
14 x 21-8

plant ledge

skylt.

decor. ceiling

MBr 1
14 x 11-8

lin.

L

DN

10'-6" clg. ht.

D   W

Foy

Br 3
11 x 11-4

Br 2
11-4 x 12-4

Garage
20-4 x 21-4

48'-0"

51'-0"

Floor Plan
No. 20154

No. 92531
Enhanced by a Columned Porch

■ This plan features:
— Three bedrooms
— Two full baths

■ A Great Room with a fireplace and decorative ceiling

■ A large efficient Kitchen with Breakfast area

■ A Master Bedroom with a private Master Bath and walk-in closet

■ A formal Dining Room conveniently located near the Kitchen

■ Two additional bedrooms with walk-in closets and use of full hall bath

FIRST FLOOR — 1,754 SQ. FT.

TOTAL LIVING AREA:
1,754 SQ. FT.

No. 92531

69'-10"

53'-5"

MASTER BATH

MASTER BEDROOM
16'-0"x13'-0"

CLO.

BEDROOM #3
11'-6"x12'-0"

CLO.

PORCH
15'-2"x5'-0"

BREAKFAST/KITCHEN
16'-6"x18'-0"

UTILITY
6'-0"x9'-0"

STORAGE
16'-0"x4'-0"

BATH #2

HALL

CLO.

GREAT ROOM
16'-10"x20'-0"

DINING
12'-0"x12'-0"

GARAGE
22'-0"x21'-0"

BEDROOM #2
11'-6"x12'-6"

CLO.

PORCH
32'-0"x5'-0"

MAIN AREA

No. 10492
Special Purpose Rooms Highlight Distinctive Design

■ This plan features:
— Three/four bedrooms
— Three full baths

■ A Television Room, Den, Family Room and an upstairs Sitting Room for many individual activities

■ A well-equipped Kitchen with double bay windows, separate dining Nook, and adjoining the formal Dining Room

■ A fireplace warming the Sitting Room adjacent to the spacious Master Suite

■ A private Deck and Master Bath complete with Roman tub and room-size, walk-in closet enhance the Master Suite

■ Two smaller bedrooms connecting to a walk-through, full bath

FIRST FLOOR — 2,409 SQ. FT.
SECOND FLOOR — 2,032 SQ. FT.
GARAGE — 690 SQ. FT.

SITTING
12'-6"
X
12'-4"

MASTER SUITE
20'-4"X13'-2"

DECK

ROMAN TUB

BEDROOM 2
13'-2"
X
12'-4"

WALK-IN CLOSET

BEDROOM 3
12'-0"
X
11'-10"

OPEN TO LIVING ROOM

SKYLIGHT

UNFINISHED
30'-2"X15'-2"

SECOND FLOOR

TOTAL LIVING AREA:
4,441 SQ. FT.

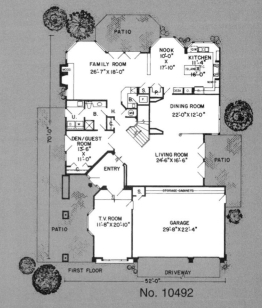

PATIO

NOOK
10'-0"
X
17'-10"

KITCHEN
11'-4"
X
16'-6"

FAMILY ROOM
26'-7"X18'-0"

DINING ROOM
22'-0"X12'-0"

DEN/GUEST ROOM
13'-6"
X
11'-0"

LIVING ROOM
24'-6"X16'-6"

PATIO

ENTRY

T.V. ROOM
11'-8"X20'-10"

STORAGE CABINETS

GARAGE
29'-8"X22'-4"

PATIO

FIRST FLOOR

DRIVEWAY

52'-0"

70'-0"

No. 10492

No. 10588
Expansive Two-Story Foyer Creates Dramatic Impression

■ This plan features:
— Four bedrooms
— Two and one half baths

■ A peninsula dividing the Kitchen from the Breakfast Nook

■ A Family Room with a fireplace just off the Breakfast area

■ A foyer linking the Living and Dining Rooms

FIRST FLOOR — 1,450 SQ. FT.
SECOND FLOOR — 1,082 SQ. FT.
BASEMENT — 1,340 SQ. FT.
GARAGE — 572 SQ. FT.

TOTAL LIVING AREA:
2,532 SQ. FT.

No. 10588

SECOND FLOOR

BEDROOM 3 11'-0" X 11'-2"
BEDROOM 4 12'-0" X 11'-2"
BEDROOM 2 12'-6" X 11'-2"
MASTER BEDROOM 13'-5" X 17'-11"
UPPER PART OF FOYER

FIRST FLOOR

DECK
2-CAR GARAGE 21'-4" X 25'-4"
DRIVE
LAUNDRY
PWDR. RM.
KIT. 10'-0" X 12'-8"
BRKFST. NOOK 9'-8" X 14'-6"
FAMILY ROOM 13'-5" X 20'-1"
LIVING ROOM 13'-5" X 19'-0"
DINING ROOM 12'-6" X 14'-7"
FOYER

No. 19422
Master Retreat Crowns Spacious Home

■ This plan features:
— Two bedrooms
— Two full baths

■ An open Foyer leading up an landing staircase with windows above and into a two-story Living Room

■ A unique four-sided fireplace separates the Living Room, Dining area and Kitchen

■ A well-equipped Kitchen featuring a cook island, a walk-in pantry and easy access to Dining area and Laundry room

■ A three season Screened Porch and Deck beyond adjoining Dining Room, Living Room, and second Bedroom

■ An private Master Suite on the second floor offering a cozy, dormer window seat, private balcony, and window tub in the spacious Bath

FIRST FLOOR — 1,290 SQ. FT.
SECOND FLOOR — 405 SQ. FT.
SCREENED PORCH — 152 SQ. FT.
GARAGE — 513 SQ. FT.

TOTAL LIVING AREA:
1,695 SQ. FT.

No. 19422

No. 24242
Savor the Summer

■ This plan features:
— Four bedrooms
— Two and a half baths

■ A efficient home with a friendly front Porch and a practical back porch

■ A cozy fireplace and a boxed window with a built-in seat in the Living Room

■ A formal Dining Room opening to front entrance and Kitchen

■ A well-equipped Kitchen with an old-fashion booth and ample cabinet and counter space adjoining Laundry area and back porch

■ A convenient, first floor Master Suite with two closet and a private Bath

■ Three additional bedrooms, on second floor, sharing a full hall bath

FIRST FLOOR — 931 SQ. FT.
SECOND FLOOR — 664 SQ. FT.

No. 24242

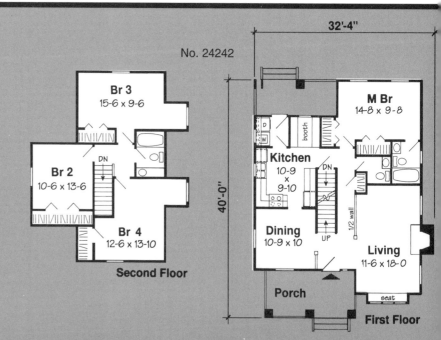

TOTAL LIVING AREA:
1,595 SQ. FT.

No. 20053
Greenhouse Brightens Three Bedroom Compact

A Karl Kreeger Design

■ This plan features:
— Three bedrooms
— Two and one half baths

■ A Kitchen including a breakfast space, a built-in desk, a pantry and compact laundry area

■ A Master Bedroom with a private, five piece bath

■ The entry and Living Room both open to the second floor, creating a bridge between the two second floor bedrooms

FIRST FLOOR — 1,088 SQ. FT.
SECOND FLOOR — 451 SQ. FT.
GREENHOUSE — 72 SQ. FT.
GARAGE — 473 SQ. FT.

TOTAL LIVING AREA: 1,539 SQ. FT.

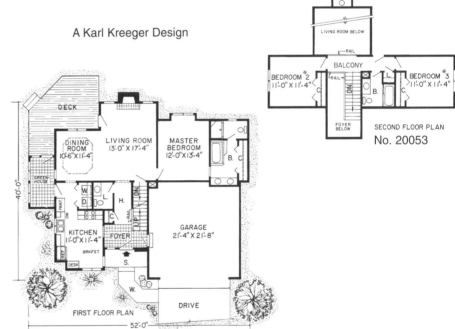

No. 20150
Sunshine Special

■ This plan features:
— Three bedrooms.
— Two full baths.
■ A Living Room with a large fireplace and sloped ceiling.
■ A walk-in closet in each bedroom
■ A Master Suite including a luxury bath and decorative ceilings.

FIRST FLOOR — 1,638 SQ. FT.
BASEMENT — 1,320 SQ. FT.
GARAGE — 462 SQ. FT.

TOTAL LIVING AREA:
1,638 SQ. FT.

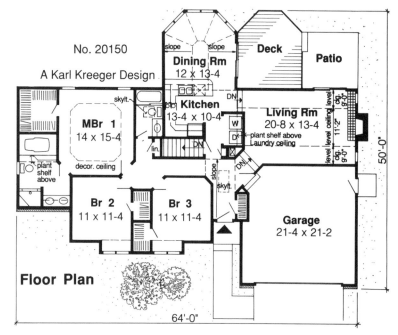

No. 20150

A Karl Kreeger Design

Floor Plan

No. 10745
Light and Airy

■ This plan features:
— Three bedrooms
— Two full baths
■ An open plan with cathedral ceilings
■ A fireplaced Great Room flowing into the Dining Room
■ A Master Bedroom with a private Master Bath
■ An efficient Kitchen with Laundry area and pantry at close proximity

FIRST FLOOR — 1,643 SQ. FT.
BASEMENT — 1,643 SQ. FT.
GARAGE — 484 SQ. FT.

TOTAL LIVING AREA:
1,643 SQ. FT.

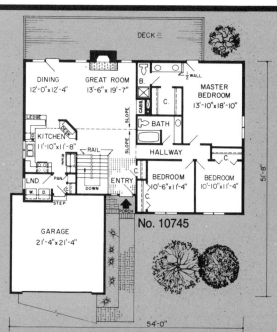

No. 10745

No. 9812
Mudroom Separates Garage, Kitchen

■ This plan features:
— Three bedrooms
— Two full and one half baths

■ An open Kitchen flowing into the Family Room

■ A Master Bedroom with private bath and ample closet space

■ A spacious, formal Living Room

■ A double Garage and storage closet in the Mudroom adding to storage area

FIRST FLOOR — 1,396 SQ. FT.
BASEMENT — 1,396 SQ. FT.
GARAGE — 484 SQ. FT.

TOTAL LIVING AREA:
1,396 SQ. FT.

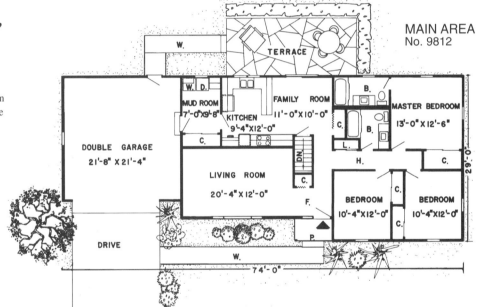

MAIN AREA
No. 9812

TERRACE

W.

W. D.

MUD ROOM
7'-0" X 9'-8"

KITCHEN
9'-4" X 12'-0"

FAMILY ROOM
11'-0" X 10'-0"

B.

MASTER BEDROOM
13'-0" X 12'-6"

C.

C.

B.

C.

DOUBLE GARAGE
21'-8" X 21'-4"

C.

DN

H.

L.

LIVING ROOM
20'-4" X 12'-0"

C.

BEDROOM
10'-4" X 12'-0"

C.

BEDROOM
10'-4" X 12'-0"

F.

C.

DRIVE

P.

W.

74'-0"

29'-0"

No. 34601
Large Front Porch Adds a Country Touch

■ This plan features:
— Three bedrooms
— Two full baths
■ A country-styled front porch
■ Vaulted ceiling in the Living Room which includes a fireplace
■ An efficient Kitchen with double sinks and peninsula counter that may double as an eating bar
■ Two first floor bedrooms with ample closet space
■ A second floor Master Suite with sloped ceiling, walk-in closet and private master Bath

FIRST FLOOR — 1,007 SQ. FT.
SECOND FLOOR — 408 SQ. FT.
BASEMENT — COMING

**TOTAL LIVING AREA:
1,415 SQ. FT.**

Alternate Foundation Plan

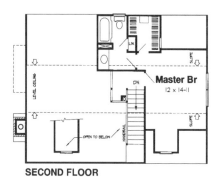

SECOND FLOOR

FIRST FLOOR
No. 34601

No. 20099
One-Floor Living

■ This plan features:
— Three bedrooms
— Two and one half baths
■ Angular windows and recessed ceilings separating the two dining areas from the adjoining island Kitchen
■ A window wall flanking the fireplace in the soaring, sky-lit Living Room
■ A Master Suite with a bump-out window and a double-vanity bath

FIRST FLOOR — 2,020 SQ. FT.
BASEMENT — 2,020 SQ. FT.
GARAGE — 534 SQ. FT.

**TOTAL LIVING AREA:
2,020 SQ. FT.**

A Karl Kreeger Design

No. 20099

No. 24402
Cathedral Ceiling in Living Room and Master Suite

■ This plan features:

— Three bedrooms

— Two full baths

■ A spacious Living Room with a cathedral ceiling and elegant fireplace

■ A Dining Room that adjoins both the Living Room and the Kitchen

■ An efficient Kitchen, with double sinks, ample cabinet space and peninsula counter that doubles as an eating bar

■ A convenient hallway laundry center

■ A Master Suite with a cathedral ceiling and a private Master Bath

MAIN AREA — 1,346 SQ. FT.

GARAGE — 449 SQ. FT.

TOTAL LIVING AREA: 1,346 SQ. FT.

No materials list available

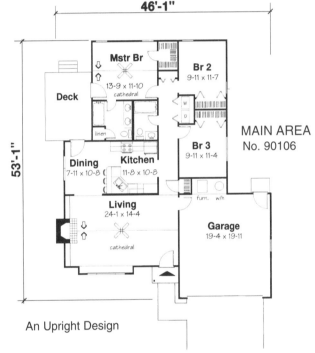

46'-1"

53'-1"

Mstr Br 13-9 x 11-10 cathedral

Deck

Br 2 9-11 x 11-7

W D

linen

Br 3 9-11 x 11-7

Dining 7-11 x 10-8

Kitchen 11-8 x 10-8

fum. w/h

Living 24-1 x 14-4 cathedral

Garage 19-4 x 19-11

MAIN AREA No. 90106

An Upright Design

No. 20058
Ranch with Character

■ This plan features:
— Three bedrooms
— Two and one half baths

■ A Master Bedroom with walk-in closet, individual shower, full tub and two-sink basin

■ A large island Kitchen with its own Breakfast area

■ A fireplaced Living Room

■ Two additional bedrooms sharing a full bath

■ A two-car Garage providing excellent additional storage

FIRST FLOOR — 1,787 SQ. FT.
BASEMENT — 1,787 SQ. FT.
GARAGE — 484 SQ. FT.

TOTAL LIVING AREA:
1,787 SQ. FT.

A Karl Kreeger Design

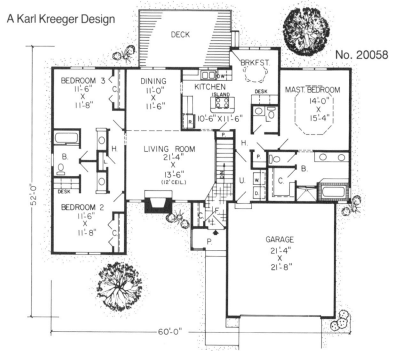

No. 20058

No. 20180
Classic Arches

■ This plan features:
— Three bedrooms
— Two full baths

■ Twin arched windows and a friendly covered porch

■ An angled entry adding intrigue to the sunny, soaring Kitchen-Breakfast Room combination accented by a rangetop island and built-in pantry

■ Living and Dining Rooms at rear of the house flowing together

FIRST FLOOR — 1,592 SQ. FT.
GARAGE — 487 SQ. FT.
BASEMENT — 1,592 SQ. FT.

TOTAL LIVING AREA:
1,592 SQ. FT.

A Karl Kreeger Design

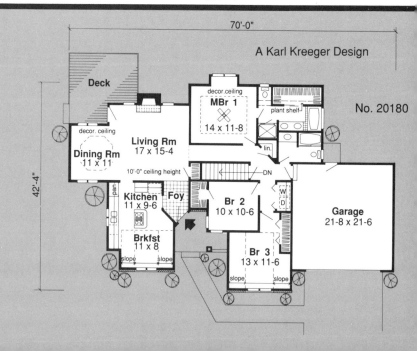

No. 20180

No. 20164
Easy Living

■ This plan features:
— Three bedrooms
— Two full baths

■ Dramatic sloped ceiling and massive fireplace in the Living Room

■ A Dining Room crowned by sloping ceiling and a plant shelf also having sliding doors to the deck

■ A U-shaped Kitchen with abundant cabinets, a window over the sink and a walk-in pantry

■ A Master Suite with a private full bath, decorative ceiling and walk-in closet

■ Two additional bedrooms that share a full bath

FIRST FLOOR — 1,456 SQ. FT.
BASEMENT — 1,448 SQ. FT.
GARAGE — 452 SQ. FT.

TOTAL LIVING AREA: 1,456 SQ. FT.

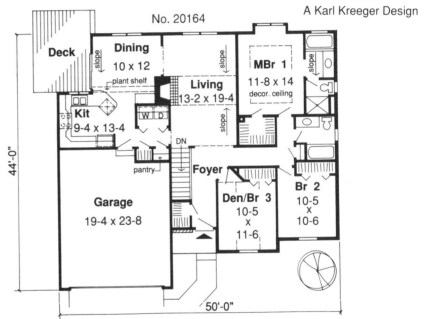

A Karl Kreeger Design

No. 20164

Deck

Dining
10 x 12

plant shelf

slope

Living
13-2 x 19-4

slope

MBr 1
11-8 x 14
decor. ceiling

slope

Kit
9-4 x 13-4

W D

DN

pantry

Foyer

Garage
19-4 x 23-8

Den/Br 3
10-5 x 11-6

Br 2
10-5 x 10-6

44'-0"

50'-0"

No. 84020
Compact And Open Cabin

■ This plan features:
— Three bedrooms
— One full bath

■ An open Living Room leading into an efficient Kitchen

■ Three bedrooms, with ample closets, sharing a full hall bath

■ A full basement option or a separate washer and dryer area

MAIN FLOOR — 768 SQ. FT.

TOTAL LIVING AREA:
768 SQ. FT.

No materials list available

Slab/Crawlspace Option

No. 84020

Br 1
opt. dining
10-6 x 8-2

Br 2
10-6 x 8-2

lin.

Living Rm
12-10 x 14-6

DN

Br 3
8 x 11-6

Kitchen
8-3 x 8

24'-0"

32'-0"

Floor Plan

No. 90106
Graceful Porch Enhances Charm

■ This plan features:
— Three bedrooms
— Two full baths

■ A formal Living Room sheltered by a railed porch

■ A hobby area including laundry facilities

■ A Kitchen, Dining, and Family Room in a "three in one" design

■ An optional basement, slab or crawl space foundation — please specify when ordering

MAIN AREA — 1,643 SQ. FT.

TOTAL LIVING AREA:
1,643 SQ. FT.

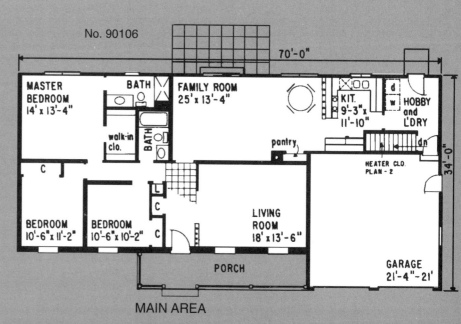

No. 90106

70'-0"

MASTER BEDROOM
14' x 13'-4"

BATH

FAMILY ROOM
25' x 13'-4"

KIT.
9'-3" x 11'-10"

HOBBY and L'DRY

walk-in clo.

BATH

pantry

c

HEATER CLO.
PLAN - 2

BEDROOM
10'-6" x 11'-2"

BEDROOM
10'-6" x 10'-2"

LIVING ROOM
18' x 13'-6"

34'-0"

GARAGE
21'-4" x 21'

PORCH

MAIN AREA

No. 90606

Traditional Elements Combine in Friendly Colonial

■ This plan features:
— Four bedrooms
— Two and one half baths

■ A beautiful circular stair ascending from the central foyer and flanked by the formal Living Room and Dining Room

■ Exposed beams, wood paneling, and a brick fireplace wall in the Family Room

■ A separate dinette opening to an efficient Kitchen

FIRST FLOOR — 1,099 SQ. FT.
SECOND FLOOR — 932 SQ. FT.

TOTAL LIVING AREA:
2,031 SQ. FT.

No. 90606

FIRST FLOOR

SECOND FLOOR

No. 91022
Double Decks Adorn Luxurious Master Suite

■ This plan features:
— Three bedrooms
— Two full and one half baths

■ Abundant windows, indoor planters and three decks uniting every room with the outdoors

■ An efficient Kitchen with direct access to the Nook and the formal Dining Room

■ A wood stove warming the spacious Family Room

■ A secluded Master Suite with private deck, Den and master Bath

■ An optional basement, slab or crawl space foundation — please specify when ordering

FIRST FLOOR — 1,985 SQ. FT.
SECOND FLOOR — 715 SQ. FT.

TOTAL LIVING AREA:
2,700 SQ. FT.

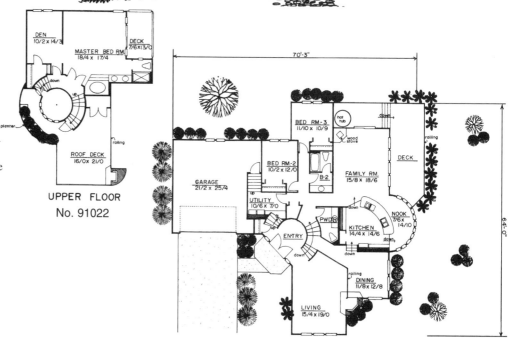

DEN
10/2 x 14/3

DECK
7/6 x13/0

MASTER BED RM
18/4 x 17/4

planter

ROOF DECK
16/0 x 21/0

railing

UPPER FLOOR
No. 91022

70'-3"

GARAGE
21/2 x 25/4

BED RM-3
11/10 x 10/9

hot tub

wood stove

DECK

BED RM-2
10/2 x 12/0

B-2

FAMILY RM.
15/8 x 18/6

UTILITY
10/6 x 7/0

PWDR

NOOK
7/6 x 14/10

KITCHEN
14/4 x 14/6

ENTRY

DINING
11/8 x 12/8

LIVING
15/4 x 19/0

64'-0"

A Westhome Planners, Ltd. Design

MAIN FLOOR

No. 24551
Distinctive Bay

■ This plan features:
— Four bedrooms
— Two full and one half baths

■ Distinctive windows and a covered entrance into a raised Foyer

■ Both the formal Living Room and Dining Room have elegant bay windows

■ A Family Room adjacent to Living Room through double doors, has a cozy fireplace and triple window view of outdoors

■ An island Kitchen with lots of counter and storage space extending into a bright Breakfast area and adjoining the Dining Room, laundry area and Garage

■ A magnificent Master Suite with a dramatic cathedral ceiling, a walk-in closet and a unusual bay window Bath featuring an atrium, and a whirlpool tub

■ Three additional bedrooms with ample closet space having easy access to a full hall bath

FIRST FLOOR — 1,324 SQ. FT.
SECOND FLOOR — 1,216 SQ. FT.

TOTAL LIVING AREA:
2,540 SQ. FT.

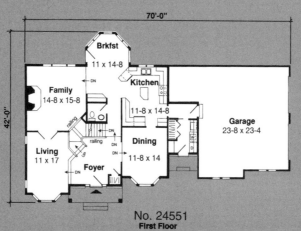

70'-0"

Brkfst
11 x 14-8

Kitchen

Family
14-8 x 15-8

11-8 x 14-8

Garage
23-8 x 23-4

Living
11 x 17

Dining
11-8 x 14

Foyer

42'-0"

No. 24551
First Floor

whirlpool

MBr
15-8 x 13

Br 2
11 x 10

shelves

railing

Br 3
11-2 x 12

open to below

Br 4
11-8 x 10-6

win. seat

books   books

Second Floor

A Britt J. Willis Design

74

No. **90844**

Open Space Living

■ This plan features:
— Three bedrooms
— Two full and one half baths

■ A wrap-around Deck providing outdoor living space, ideal for a sloping lot

■ Two and a half-story glass wall and two separate atrium doors providing natural light for the Living/Dining Room area

■ An efficient galley Kitchen with easy access to the Dining area

■ A Master Bedroom suite with a half bath and ample closet space

■ Another bedroom on the first floor adjoins a full hall bath

■ A second floor Bedroom/Studio, with a private Deck, adjacent to a full hall bath and a Loft area

FIRST FLOOR — 1,086 SQ. FT.
SECOND FLOOR — 466 SQ. FT.

TOTAL LIVING AREA:
1,552 SQ. FT.

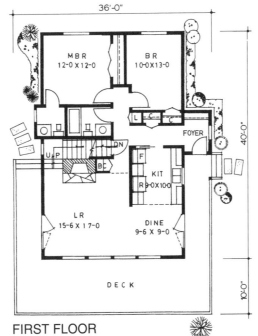

FIRST FLOOR

36'-0"

MBR
12-0 X 12-0

BR
10-0 X 13-0

FOYER

40'-0"

UP

DN

BC

F

KIT
R 9-0X10-0

LR
15-6 X 17-0

DINE
9-6 X 9-0

10'-0"

DECK

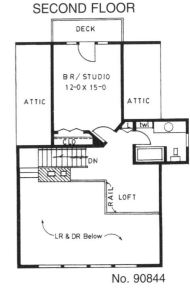

SECOND FLOOR

DECK

BR/STUDIO
12-0 X 15-0

ATTIC

ATTIC

CLO

twl

DN

RAIL

LOFT

LR & DR Below

No. **90844**

No. 90905
Compact Home is Surprisingly Spacious

■ This plan features:
— Three bedrooms
— Two full baths

■ A spacious Living Room warmed by a fireplace

■ A Dining Room flowing off the Living Room, with sliding glass doors to the deck

■ An efficient, well-equipped Kitchen with a snack bar, double sink, and ample cabinet and counter space

■ A Master Suite with a walk-in closet and private full bath

■ Two additional, roomy bedrooms with ample closet space and protection from street noise from the two-car garage

MAIN AREA — 1,314 SQ. FT.
BASEMENT — 1,488 SQ. FT.
GARAGE — 484 SQ. FT.
WIDTH — 50'-0"
DEPTH — 54'-0"

A Westhome Planners, Ltd. Design

TOTAL LIVING AREA:
1,314 SQ. FT.

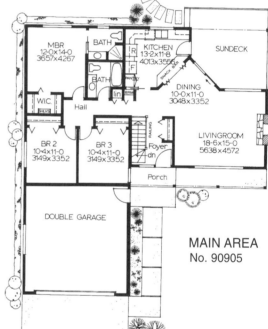

MAIN AREA
No. 90905

No. 91706
Master Suite is Home Away from Home

■ This plan features:
— Three bedrooms
— Two full and one half baths

■ A secluded, second floor Master Suite with sky-lit Master Bath, laundry chute, private study and a corner fireplace

■ A pre-fabricated Solarium, doubling the size of the bright Kitchen/Family Room

■ An elegant Living Room with a corner fireplace and large front windows

■ A formal Dining Room conveniently located next to the Kitchen

■ Two additional bedrooms that are served by a full hall bath

FIRST FLOOR — 1,856 SQ. FT.
SECOND FLOOR — 618 SQ. FT.
GARAGE — 704 SQ. FT.

No. 91706

TOTAL LIVING AREA:
2,474 SQ. FT.

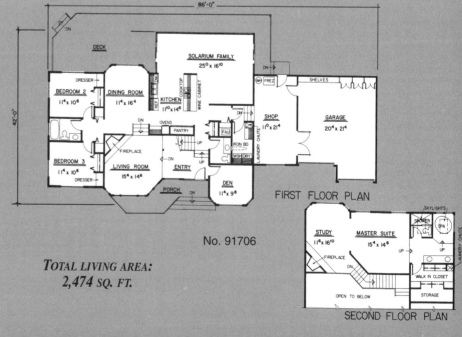

No. 93523
Colonial Charmer

■ This plan features:
— Four bedrooms
— Two full and one half baths
■ An oversized Family Room that opens into the Kitchen/Nook area creating a feeling of space
■ A large fireplace and access to the patio in the Family Room
■ A peninsula counter and double sinks as well as an abundance of counter and cupboard space in the Kitchen
■ A formal Living Room and Dining Room for entertaining
■ A Master Suite that includes two closets, a jacuzzi and double vanity
■ Three additional bedrooms, one with a walk-in closet, that share a full hall bath

FIRST FLOOR — 970 SQ. FT.
SECOND FLOOR — 950 SQ. FT.
BASEMENT — 970 SQ. FT.
GARAGE — 462 SQ. FT.
FOUNDATION — BASEMENT OR CRAWL SPACE

SECOND FLOOR

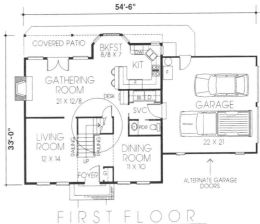

FIRST FLOOR

No. 93523

TOTAL LIVING AREA:
1,920 SQ. FT.

OPTIONAL BASEMENT

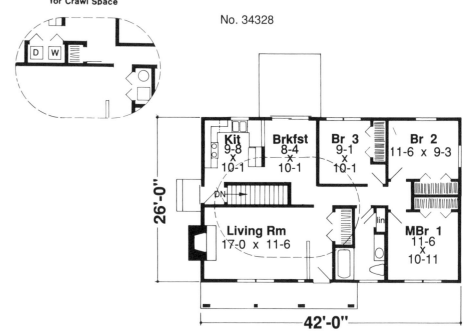

No. 34328
Compact Ranch Loaded with Living Space

- ■ This plan features:
- — Three bedrooms
- — One full bath
- ■ A central entrance opening to the Living Room with ample windows
- ■ A Kitchen featuring a dining area with sliding doors to the backyard and optional deck
- ■ An optional slab or crawl space foundation — please specify when ordering

FIRST FLOOR — 1,092 SQ. FT.
BASEMENT — 1,092 SQ. FT.

**TOTAL LIVING AREA:
1,092 SQ. FT.**

ALTERNATE FLOOR PLAN
for Crawl Space

No. 34328

Kit 9-8 x 10-1
Brkfst 8-4 x 10-1
Br 3 9-1 x 10-1
Br 2 11-6 x 9-3
Living Rm 17-0 x 11-6
MBr 1 11-6 x 10-11
DN
26'-0"
42'-0"

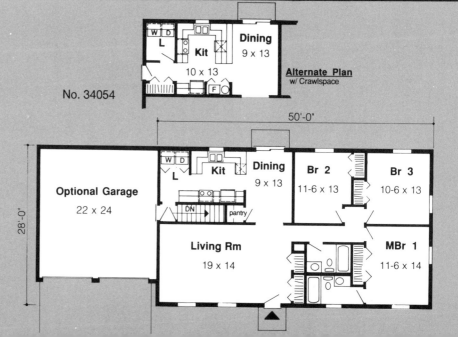

No. 34054
Ranch Provides Great Kitchen Area

- ■ This plan features:
- — Three bedrooms
- — Two full baths
- ■ A Dining Room with sliding glass doors to backyard
- ■ Access to the Garage through the laundry room
- ■ A Master Bedroom with private full bath
- ■ An optional two car Garage
- ■ An optional basement or crawl space foundation available — please specify when ordering

FIRST FLOOR — 1,400 SQ. FT.
BASEMENT — 1,400 SQ. FT.
GARAGE — 528 SQ. FT.

**TOTAL LIVING AREA:
1,400 SQ. FT.**

W D L Kit 10 x 13 Dining 9 x 13
Alternate Plan w/ Crawlspace
No. 34054

50'-0"

Optional Garage 22 x 24
W D L Kit Dining 9 x 13 Br 2 11-6 x 13 Br 3 10-6 x 13
DN pantry
Living Rm 19 x 14
MBr 1 11-6 x 14
28'-0"

No. 20204
Abundance of Closet Space

■ This plan features:
— Three bedrooms
— Two full baths

■ Roomy walk-in closets in all bedrooms

■ A Master Bedroom with decorative ceiling and a private full bath

■ A fireplaced Living Room with sloped ceilings and sliders to the deck

■ An efficient Kitchen with plenty of cupboard space and a pantry

FIRST FLOOR —1,532 SQ. FT.
GARAGE — 484 SQ. FT.

TOTAL LIVING AREA:
1,532 SQ. FT.

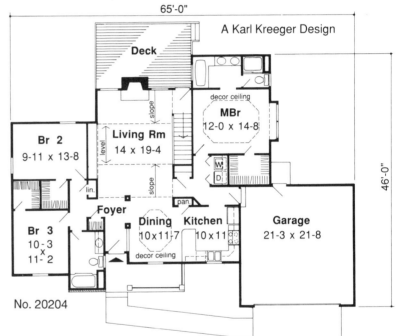

A Karl Kreeger Design

65'-0"

46'-0"

Deck

Living Rm
14 x 19-4

MBr
12-0 x 14-8
decor ceiling

Br 2
9-11 x 13-8

lin.

W
D

Foyer

Br 3
10-3 x 11-2

Dining
10 x 11-7
decor ceiling

Kitchen
10 x 11

pan.

Garage
21-3 x 21-8

No. 20204

No. 22004
Brick Home with Four Bedrooms

■ This plan features:
— Four bedrooms
— Two and one half baths
■ Four roomy bedrooms, including the Master Bedroom
■ A centrally located Family Room including a fireplace, wet bar, and access to the patio
■ A large Dining Room at the front of the home for entertaining
■ An interesting Kitchen and Nook with an adjoining Utility room

FIRST FLOOR — 2,070 SQ. FT.
GARAGE — 474 SQ. FT.

TOTAL LIVING AREA: 2,070 SQ. FT.

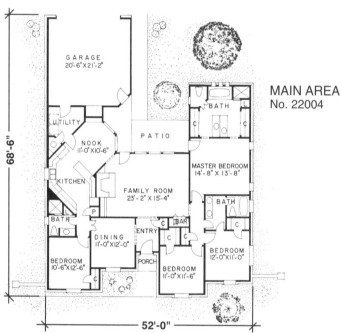

MAIN AREA
No. 22004

No. 10518
Compact Design, Ample Space

■ This plan features:
— Three bedrooms
— Two baths
■ A combined Living/Dining Room opening to a deck
■ A Kitchen easily accessible from the entry
■ A Master Bedroom with its own private bath

FIRST FLOOR — 864 SQ. FT.
SECOND FLOOR — 307 SQ. FT.

TOTAL LIVING AREA: 1,171 SQ. FT.

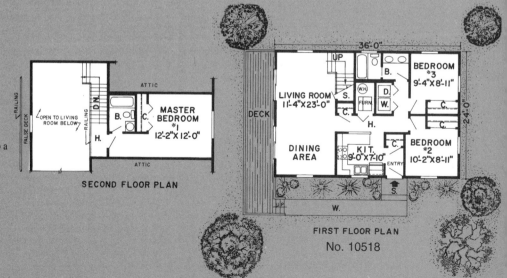

SECOND FLOOR PLAN

FIRST FLOOR PLAN
No. 10518

No. 9964
Recreation Room Houses Fireplace

■ This plan features:

— Four bedrooms

— Two full baths

■ A wood-burning fireplace warming the Living/Dining Room, which is accessible to the large wooden sun deck

■ Two first-floor bedrooms with access to a full hall bath

■ Two ample-sized second floor bedrooms

■ A Recreation Room with a cozy fireplace and convenient half bath

FIRST FLOOR — 896 SQ. FT.

SECOND FLOOR — 457 SQ. FT.

BASEMENT — 864 SQ. FT.

TOTAL LIVING AREA:
1,353 SQ. FT.

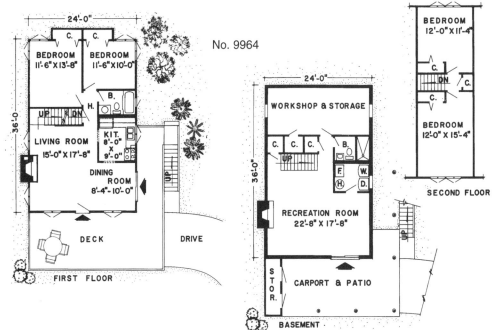

No. 9964

No. 10376
Underground Delight

■ This plan features:
— Three bedrooms
— Two full baths

■ A design that aids against the high cost of living through many energy-saving features including the use of passive solar energy

■ Sliding glass doors leading to the front lawn from all three bedrooms

■ A large eat in Kitchen open to the Family Room and near the Utility Room

■ Added features including a greenhouse, Sewing Room and Jacuzzi in the Master Bathroom

FIRST FLOOR — 2,086 SQ. FT.

TOTAL LIVING AREA:
2,086 SQ. FT.

No. 10376

No. 10619
Deck Doubles Outdoor Living Space

■ This plan features:
— Three bedrooms
— Three baths

■ A design made for the sun lover with a front deck and patio

■ A sunken Living Room with three window walls and a massive fireplace.

■ A hot tub with skylight, a vaulted Master Suite and a utility area

FIRST FLOOR — 2,352 SQ. FT.
BASEMENT — 2,352 SQ. FT.
GARAGE — 696 SQ. FT.

TOTAL LIVING AREA:
2,352 SQ. FT.

A Karl Kreeger Design

No. 10619

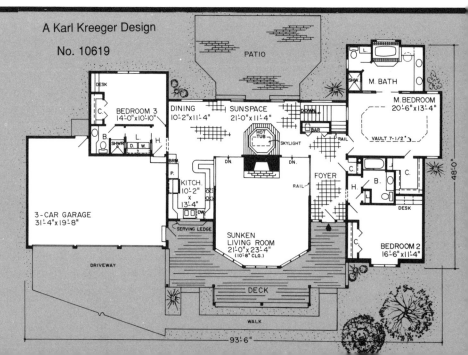

No. 20089
Carefree Living on One Level

■ This plan features:
— Three bedrooms
— Two full baths
■ A full basement and an oversized two-car Garage
■ A spacious Master Suite with a walk-in closet
■ A fireplaced Living Room, an open Dining Room and Kitchen for convenience

MAIN AREA — 1,588 SQ. FT.
BASEMENT — 780 SQ. FT.
GARAGE — 808 SQ. FT.

TOTAL LIVING AREA:
1,588 SQ. FT.

A Karl Kreegar Design

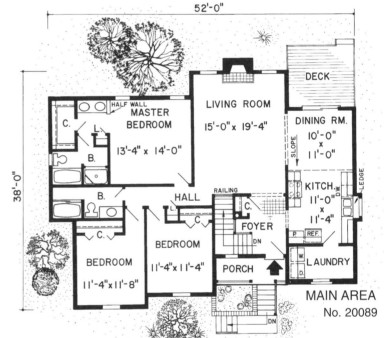

52'-0"

38'-0"

DECK

LIVING ROOM
15'-0" x 19'-4"

MASTER BEDROOM
13'-4" x 14'-0"

HALF WALL

C.

B.

B.

DINING RM.
10'-0" x 11'-0"

SLOPE

KITCH.
11'-0" x 11'-4"

DW

LEDGE

HALL

RAILING

C.

FOYER

DN

P REF.

BEDROOM
11'-4" x 11'-4"

C.

BEDROOM
11'-4" x 11'-8"

C.

PORCH

W
D

LAUNDRY

DN

MAIN AREA
No. 20089

No. 24404
Influence by Yesteryear

■ This plan features:
— Three bedrooms
— Three full baths

■ A country wrap-around porch welcoming guests with shelter

■ A Foyer area with a coat closet and graceful staircase

■ A tray ceiling topping the elegant formal Dining Room with a double door entrance to the Kitchen

■ A large Kitchen with a center work island/eating bar and a built-in desk plus more than ample counter and storage space

■ An expansive Family Room with a large fireplace and built-in book shelves as well as a tray ceiling

■ A vaulted ceiling in the Master Suite further enhanced by a lavish bath and a walk-in closet

■ Two additional bedrooms that share the use of a full bath in the hall

FIRST FLOOR — 1,236 SQ. FT.
SECOND FLOOR — 1,120 SQ. FT.

Crawl Space / Slab Option

Optional Kitchen

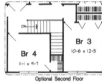

Optional Second Floor

An Upright Design

Second Floor

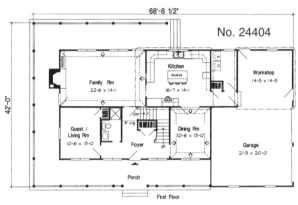

No. 24404

First Floor

TOTAL LIVING AREA:
2,356 SQ. FT.

No materials list available

No. 91731
Country Style Charm

■ This plan features:
— Three bedrooms
— Two full baths

■ Brick accents, front facing gable, and railed wrap-around covered porch

■ A built-in range and oven in a dog-leg shaped Kitchen

■ A Nook with garage access for convenient unloading of groceries and other supplies

■ A bay window wrapping around the front of the formal Living Room

■ A Master Suite with French doors opening to the deck

MAIN AREA — 1,775 SQ. FT.
GARAGE — 681 SQ. FT.
WIDTH — 51'-6"
DEPTH — 65'-0"

TOTAL LIVING AREA:
1,775 SQ. FT.

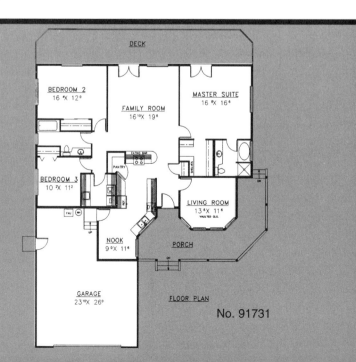

FLOOR PLAN

No. 91731

No. 84037
Tudor Facade Graces Convenient Plan

■ This plan features:
— Three bedrooms
— Two and one half baths

■ A tiled two-story foyer opening to the Family Room which includes a fireplace and 10-foot ceilings

■ An open Kitchen/Breakfast area adjoining the Dining Room and the outdoor deck

■ A first floor Master Bedroom with a private bath and a huge walk-in closet

■ A two-car Garage with entrance through a convenient utility room

■ An optional slab, crawl space or basement foundation available — please specify when ordering

FIRST FLOOR — 1,880 SQ. FT.
SECOND FLOOR — 575 SQ. FT.
GARAGE — 594 SQ. FT.

TOTAL LIVING AREA:
2,455 SQ. FT.

No materials list available

Br 3
11-0 x13-4

skylight

lin.

dn. attic

Br 2
12-0 x13-4

open to foyer

Second Floor

No. 84037

Slab/Crawlspace Option

optional Fireplace

optional Deck

Family Rm
16-0 x23-4
(10' ceil.)

U.

dw

Kit/Brkfst
18-8x 13-4

lin.

M. Bedroom
16-0 x13-4

52'0"

pan.   desk

dn.

Dining Rm
12-0 x13-0

up

Foyer

Living Rm
13-0 x 15-4

Garage
22-4 x25-4

First Floor

67'0"

No. 9714
Excellent Choice for Sloping Lot

■ This plan features:
— Three bedrooms
— Three full baths
■ A Family Room on the lower level facing the front, and opening onto the lower level
■ A sun deck on the upper level adjoining the Living and Dining Rooms
■ A tiled country Kitchen with a cooking island and a built-in laundry room

FIRST FLOOR — 1,748 SQ. FT.
SECOND FLOOR — 932 SQ. FT.
GARAGE — 768 SQ. FT.

TOTAL LIVING AREA:
2,680 SQ. FT.

No. 9714

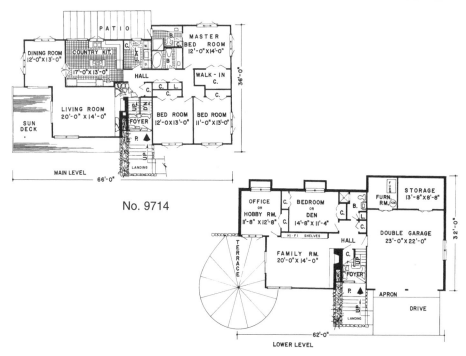

No. 20211
Inspired by Country Porches of Old

■ This plan features:
— Three bedrooms
— Two full baths
■ Decorative and sloped ceilings
■ A large Kitchen with a central island, a double sink, a pantry, as well as ample cabinet and counter space
■ A Master Suite with a decorative ceiling, and a walk-in closet
■ A decorative ceiling in the Dining Room
■ A central, focal-point fireplace and sloped ceilings in the Living Room
■ Two additional bedrooms that share use of a full hall bath

MAIN AREA — 1,609 SQ. FT.

TOTAL LIVING AREA:
1,609 SQ. FT.

A Karl Kreeger Design

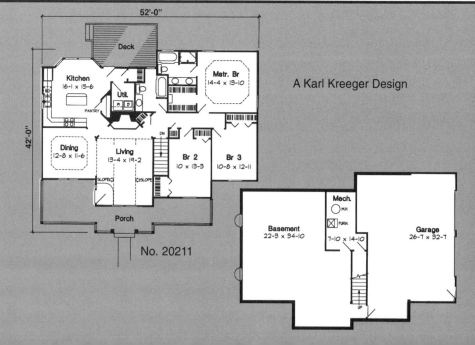

No. 20211

No. 20148
Hillside Haven

■ This plan features:

— Three bedrooms

— Two full baths

■ A well-appointed Kitchen that adjoins a cheerful, six-sided Breakfast Room with access to the wrap-around deck

■ A decorative ceiling in the formal Dining Room which flows into the Living Room

■ A sky-lit Living Room with a built-in wetbar and a fireplace

■ A Master Suite with a decorative ceiling, a window seat, a walk-in closet, and a private Master Bath

■ Two additional bedrooms with ample closet space that share a full hall bath

FIRST FLOOR — 1,774 SQ. FT.

BASEMENT — 1,399 SQ. FT.

GARAGE — 551 SQ. FT.

TOTAL LIVING AREA:
1,774 SQ. FT.

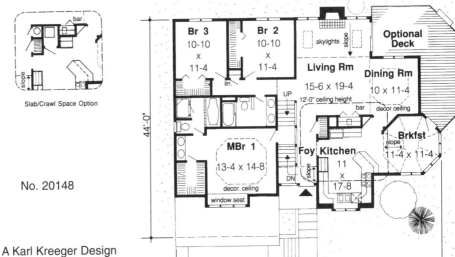

Slab/Crawl Space Option

No. 20148

A Karl Kreeger Design

Br 3
10-10
x
11-4

Br 2
10-10
x
11-4

skylights
slope

Optional Deck

Living Rm
15-6 x 19-4

12'-0" ceiling height

Dining Rm
10 x 11-4

decor ceiling

UP

bar

Brkfst
11-4 x 11-4
slope

MBr 1
13-4 x 14-8

decor. ceiling

window seat

Foy

DN

Kitchen
11
x
17-8

lin.

44'-0"

56'-0"

No. 10734

Sunny and Warm

A Karl Kreeger Design

■ This plan features:
— Four bedrooms
— Three full baths and two half baths
■ The children's rooms upstairs, sharing a full bath with a double vanity and just steps away from a loft ideal for a playroom
■ An island cook top, loads of counter space and a Breakfast nook in the Kitchen
■ A Deck, Sun Room, and Utility room
■ A Master Bedroom with a fireplace, a walk-in closet and a Study

FIRST FLOOR — 2,887 SQ. FT.
SECOND FLOOR — 1,488 SQ. FT.
BASEMENT — 2,888 SQ. FT.
GARAGE — 843 SQ. FT.

TOTAL LIVING AREA: 4,375 SQ. FT.

No. 10734

SECOND FLOOR

FIRST FLOOR

No. 92515

Elegant and Efficient

TOTAL LIVING AREA: 1,959 SQ. FT.

■ This plan features:
— Three bedrooms
—Two full baths
■ Covered entrance into the Foyer leads to a spacious Den with a decorative ceiling above a hearth fireplace and French doors to the patio area
■ Decorative window and ceiling highlight the formal Dining Room
■ Large, country Kitchen with double ovens, a cooktop and a peninsula snackbar serving the bright Breakfast area
■ Large Master Bedroom suite with a decorative ceiling, a walk-in closet and a plush bath with a double vanity and a whirlpool tub
■ Two additional bedrooms with walk-in closets share a full bath
■ This plan is available with a Slab or Crawlspace foundation. Please specify when ordering
MAIN FLOOR — 1,959 SQ. FT.
GARAGE — 484 SQ. FT.

No. 92515

No. 24245
Wrap-Around Country Porch Provides a Warm Welcome

- This plan features:
  - Three bedrooms
  - Two full and one half baths
- Formal areas flanking the entry hall
- A Living Room that includes a wonderful fireplace
- Direct access from the formal Dining Room to the Kitchen
- A U-shaped Kitchen including a breakfast bar, built-in pantry and planning desk and a double sink
- A Mudroom entry that will help keep the dirt from play or muddy shoes away from the rest of the home
- A sunny Breakfast Nook providing a cheerful place to start your day
- An expansive Family Room with direct access to the rear wood deck
- A Master Suite highlighted by a walk-in closet and a private Master Bath
- Two additional bedrooms, one with a built-in desk, share a full hall bath with a double vanity

FIRST FLOOR — 1,095 SQ. FT.
SECOND FLOOR — 952 SQ. FT.
GARAGE — 480 SQ. FT.
BASEMENT — 1,095 SQ. FT.

TOTAL LIVING AREA:
2,047 SQ. FT.

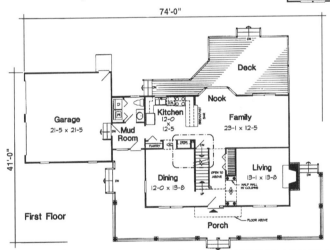

First Floor

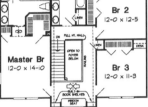

Second Floor

Crawl Space/Slab Option

No. 24245

No. 20054
Striking Entryway

■ This plan features:

— Two bedrooms, with optional third bedroom/den

— Two full baths

■ A cathedral ceiling gracing the Living Room

■ A large Master Bedroom with an ample closet and a full Master Bath

■ A Dining Room with an attractive decorative ceiling

■ A modern Kitchen flowing into the Breakfast area

■ A conveniently located laundry area

MAIN AREA — 1,461 SQ. FT.

BASEMENT — 1,458 SQ. FT.

GARAGE — 528 SQ. FT.

TOTAL LIVING AREA:
1,461 SQ. FT.

MAIN AREA
No. 20054
A Karl Kreeger Design

No. 90622
Two-Sink Baths Ease Rush

■ This plan features:

— Four bedrooms

— Two full and one half baths

■ A wood beam ceiling in the spacious Family Room

■ An efficient, island Kitchen with a sunny bay window dinette

■ A formal Living Room with a heat-circulating fireplace

■ A large Master Suite with a walk-in closet and a private Master Bath

■ Three additional bedrooms sharing a full hall bath

FIRST FLOOR — 983 SQ. FT.

SECOND FLOOR — 1,013 SQ. FT.

MUDROOM — 99 SQ. FT.

GARAGE — 481 SQ. FT.

TOTAL LIVING AREA:
2,095 SQ. FT.

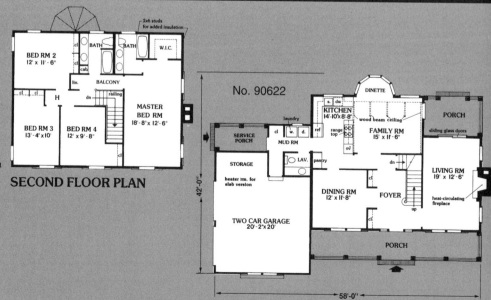

No. 90622

SECOND FLOOR PLAN

FIRST FLOOR PLAN

No. 20187
Ranch with Everything

A Karl Kreeger Design

■ This plan features:
— Three bedrooms
— Two full baths

■ A decorative ceiling in the elegant formal Dining Room

■ A well-appointed Kitchen with built-in pantry, ample counter space and peninsula island that separates the Kitchen from the Breakfast room

■ A Living Room, with easy access to the deck made cozy by a fireplace

■ A Master Bedroom with private Master Bath and walk-in closet

■ Two additional bedrooms that share a full hall bath

MAIN AREA — 1,416 SQ. FT.
BASEMENT — 1,416 SQ. FT.
GARAGE — 484 SQ. FT.

TOTAL LIVING AREA:
1,416 SQ. FT.

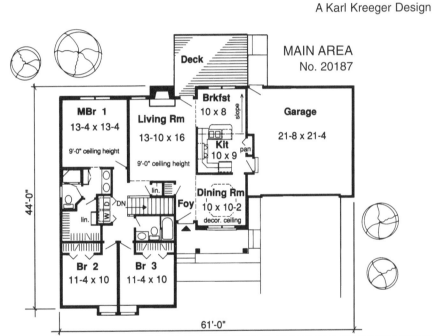

MAIN AREA
No. 20187

Deck

Brkfst
10 x 8

MBr 1
13-4 x 13-4
9'-0" ceiling height

Living Rm
13-10 x 16
9'-0" ceiling height

Kit
10 x 9

pan

Garage
21-8 x 21-4

DN

lin.

W D

lin.

Foy

Dining Rm
10 x 10-2
decor. ceiling

Br 2
11-4 x 10

Br 3
11-4 x 10

44'-0"

61'-0"

No. 90613
Year Round Retreat

■ This plan features:
— Three bedrooms
— Two full baths

■ A Living Room with a dramatic sloping ceiling and a wood burning stove

■ A Kitchen and Living Room opening onto the rear deck

■ A Master Suite with a full bath, linen closet and ample closet space

FIRST FLOOR — 967 SQ. FT.
SECOND FLOOR — 465 SQ. FT.

TOTAL LIVING AREA:
1,432 SQ. FT.

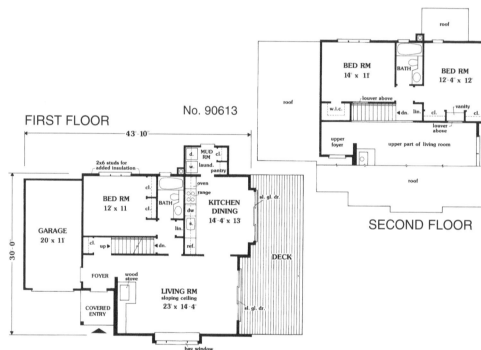

FIRST FLOOR   No. 90613

SECOND FLOOR

No. 24561
A Dramatic Entrance

■ This plan features:
— Three bedrooms
— Two and a half baths

■ A eye-catching entrance with sidelights and an attractive window illuminating the two story Foyer

■ A formal Dining Room flowing easily from the Kitchen

■ An island work station, double sink, walk-in pantry and more than ample counter space in the Kitchen

■ A hip vaulted ceiling adorning the Breakfast Area

■ A large Family Room enhanced by a corner fireplace with built-in wood storage

■ A Sun Room that creates a bright airy place to relax in

■ A Master Suite with a double vanity bath and walk-in closet

FIRST FLOOR — 1,675 SQ. FT.
SECOND FLOOR — 1,284 SQ. FT.

TOTAL LIVING AREA:
2,959 SQ. FT.

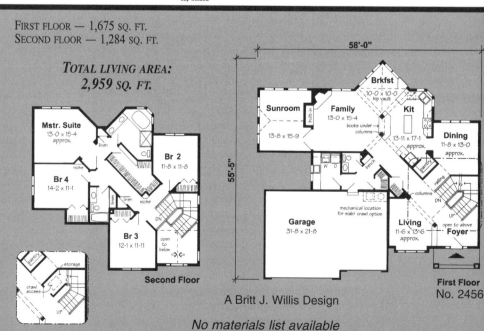

A Britt J. Willis Design

No materials list available

No. 90107

Open Living Area, Plus
Traditional Styling

■ This plan features:
— Two bedrooms
— Two full baths

■ A Great Room concept that combines the Kitchen, Dining and Living Rooms

■ An efficient U-shaped Kitchen, equipped with a double sink and plenty of cupboard and counter space

■ A Dining Room that has direct access to the rear patio, expanding living spaces in warmer months

■ A Master Bedroom with a walk-in closet and a private bath

■ A second bedroom that has use of the full hall bath

■ A two-car garage with plenty of storage space

■ An optional basement, slab or crawlspace foundation — please specify when ordering

MAIN AREA — 1,092 SQ. FT.

TOTAL LIVING AREA:
1,092 SQ. FT.

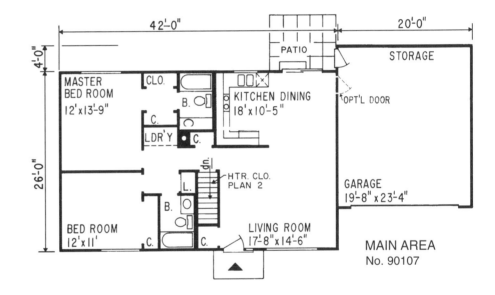

MAIN AREA
No. 90107

No. 8262
Fabulous Fieldstone Contemporary

■ This plan features:
— Three bedrooms
— Two full baths

■ Sheltered entrance into expansive Living Room with corner fireplace and a wall of windows

■ Convenient Dining Room with built-in planter, opens to Living Room, Screened Porch and Kitchen

■ Efficient, L-shaped Kitchen with built-in dinette and access to back yard

■ Three bedrooms, one with a private bath, have ample closets and large sliding windows

■ Double Garage with room for storage and access to Screened Porch

MAIN FLOOR — 1,406 SQ. FT.
SCREENED PORCH — 107 SQ. FT.
BASEMENT — 1,394 SQ. FT.
GARAGE — 426 SQ. FT.

TOTAL LIVING AREA:
1,406 SQ. FT.

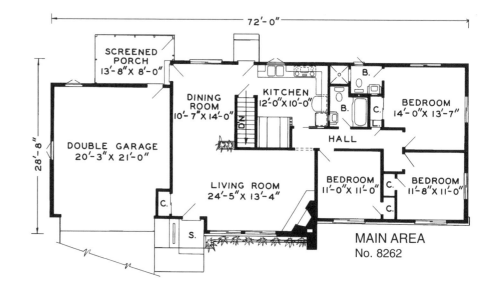

SCREENED PORCH 13'-8" X 8'-0"

DINING ROOM 10'-7" X 14'-0"

KITCHEN 12'-0" X 10'-0"

B.
B.
C.

BEDROOM 14'-0" X 13'-7"

DOUBLE GARAGE 20'-3" X 21'-0"

HALL

LIVING ROOM 24'-5" X 13'-4"

BEDROOM 11'-0" X 11'-0"

BEDROOM 11'-8" X 11'-0"

C.
C.
C.

C.
S.

72'-0"
28'-8"

MAIN AREA
No. 8262

No. 20199
The Perfect Home

■ This plan features:
— Four bedrooms
— Three and one half baths

■ A stunning fireplace in the Breakfast/Hearth Room with a built-in TV cabinet and plant shelf

■ A spacious Living Room with ten-foot ceiling height

■ A decorative ceiling enhancing the elegant Dining Room

■ An efficient Kitchen with all the amenities

■ A sloped ceiling in the Master Suite and a private full bath with walk-in closet

■ Three additional bedrooms, one with a private bath and two with walk-in closets

FIRST FLOOR — 1,760 SQ. FT.
SECOND FLOOR — 785 SQ. FT.
BASEMENT — 1,760 SQ. FT.
GARAGE — 797 SQ. FT.

TOTAL LIVING AREA:
2,545 SQ. FT.

Second Floor

Br 4
11-4 x 10

Br 2
12 x 13-4

Br 3
11 x 13

A Karl Kreegar Design

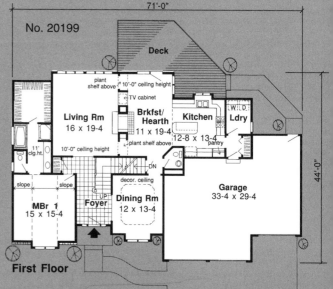

No. 20199

Deck

Living Rm
16 x 19-4

Brkfst/ Hearth
11 x 19-4

Kitchen
12-8 x 13-4

Ldry

Garage
33-4 x 29-4

MBr 1
15 x 15-4

Foyer

Dining Rm
12 x 13-4

First Floor

71'-0"
44'-0"

No. 20105
Timeless Elegance

■ This plan features:
— Four bedrooms
— Three and one half baths

■ A handsome Tudor exterior

■ A foyer flanked by a formal Dining Room and a Library

■ A massive Living Room enhanced by high ceilings, abundant windows, and access to a rear deck

■ The Living and Hearth Rooms sharing a fireplace and wetbar creating a convenient atmosphere for entertaining

■ A Kitchen with a handy breakfast bar and pantry

■ A first-floor Master Suite with recessed ceilings, twin walk-in closets, and a luxurious bath

FIRST FLOOR — 2,080 SQ. FT.
SECOND FLOOR — 1,051 SQ. FT.
BASEMENT — 2,080 SQ. FT.
GARAGE — 666 SQ. FT.

TOTAL LIVING AREA:
3,131 SQ. FT.

A Karl Kreeger Design

No. 20105

No. 10805
Today's Features, Yesterday's Old-Fashioned Charm

■ This plan features:
— Three bedrooms
— Two and one half baths
■ Wide corner boards, clapboard siding, and a full-length covered porch lending a friendly air to this classic home
■ A central entry opening to a cozy Den on the right, a sunken Living Room with adjoining Dining Room on the left
■ An informal Dining Nook accented by bay windows
■ A Master Suite spanning the rear of the home including a huge, walk-in closet, a private bath with double vanities, and a whirlpool tub

FIRST FLOOR — 1,622 SQ. FT.
SECOND FLOOR — 1,156 SQ. FT.

TOTAL LIVING AREA: 2,778 SQ. FT.

Second Floor

First Floor
No. 10805

No. 10649
Room for Family Activities

■ This plan features:
— Three bedrooms
— Two and one half baths
■ A Family Room warmed with a fireplace, lots of windows, French doors, wet bar and access to the covered porch
■ A Kitchen centered between a bay window breakfast nook and a formal Dining Room
■ Window seats adorning the front bedrooms

FIRST FLOOR — 1,285 SQ. FT.
SECOND FLOOR — 930 SQ. FT.
GARAGE — 492 SQ. FT.

TOTAL LIVING AREA: 2,215 SQ. FT.

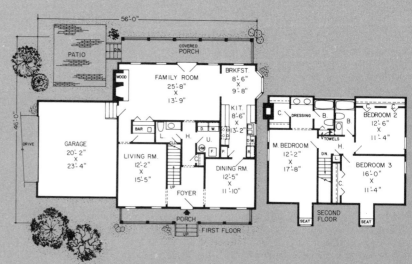

No. 10649

No. 24260
Spacious Great Room Provides Center of Activity

■ This plan features:
  – Three bedrooms
  – Two full baths

■ A spacious Great Room which dominates the center of the home with a built-in entertainment center and a fireplace

■ A secluded Master Suite including a private Master Bath with a double vanity, a corner oval tub, separate shower and a large walk-in closet

■ An efficient Kitchen with a built-in pantry, peninsula eating bar and an eating Nook

■ A formal Dining Room with a butler's pantry located at the entrance of the room

■ Two additional bedrooms that share a full hall bath

FIRST FLOOR — 2,010 SQ. FT.

GARAGE — 482 SQ. FT.

TOTAL LIVING AREA:
2,010 SQ. FT.

No. 24260

No materials list available

An Energetic Enterprises Design

No. 20526
Exciting Ceilings and Terraces

■ This plan features:
— Three bedrooms
— Two full baths

■ A foyer leading into the Family Room with sloped ceilings

■ A U-shaped Kitchen with space for informal meals

■ A Dining Room separated from the Living Room, but with the warmth from the fireplace reaching the table

■ A Dining Room with access to the terrace through sliding doors

■ A Master Bedroom with a high tray ceiling, a private bath, and sliders to a private terrace

FIRST FLOOR — 1,633 SQ. FT.
BASEMENT — 1,633 SQ. FT.
GARAGE — 423 SQ. FT.

TOTAL LIVING AREA:
1,633 SQ. FT.

Floor Plan

No. 20526

No. 20104
Easy One Level Living

■ This plan features:
— Three bedrooms
— Two full baths

■ A sky-lit Kitchen

■ Ample closet space

■ Built-in storage areas in Kitchen

■ A Master bath with twin vanities, raised tub, and walk in shower

FIRST FLOOR — 1,686 SQ. FT.
BASEMENT — 1,677 SQ. FT.
GARAGE — 475 SQ. FT.

TOTAL LIVING AREA:
1,686 SQ. FT.

A Karl Kreeger Design

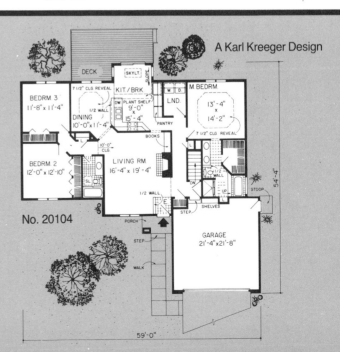

No. 20104

No. 20087
Foyer Isolates Bedroom Wing

■ This plan features:
— Three bedrooms
— Two full baths

■ A Living Room complete with a window-wall flanking a massive fireplace

■ A Dining Room with recessed ceilings and a pass through for convenience

■ A Master Suite tucked behind the two-car Garage for maximum noise protection

■ A spacious Kitchen with built-ins and access to the two-car Garage

FIRST FLOOR — 1,568 SQ. FT.
BASEMENT — 1,568 SQ. FT.
GARAGE — 484 SQ. FT.

TOTAL LIVING AREA:
1,568 SQ. FT.

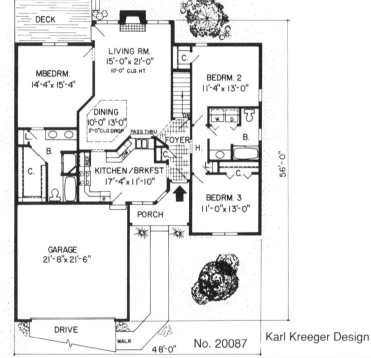

No. 20087   Karl Kreeger Design

No. 10394
Master Suite Crowns Plan

■ This plan features:
— Three bedrooms
— Two full baths
■ A Master Bedroom which occupies the entire second level
■ A passive solar design
■ A Living Room which rises two stories in the front
■ Skylights in the sloping ceilings of the Kitchen and Master Bath

FIRST FLOOR — 1,306 SQ. FT.
SECOND FLOOR — 472 SQ. FT.
GARAGE — 576 SQ. FT.

TOTAL LIVING AREA: 1,778 SQ. FT.

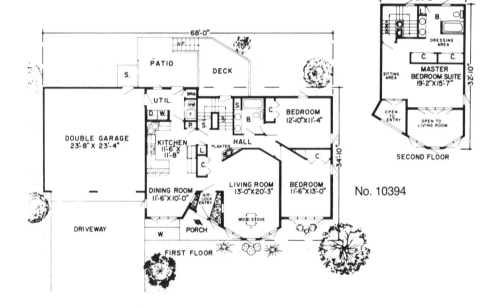

No. 10394

No. 1078
Vacation Retreat or Year Round Living

■ This plan features:
— Two bedrooms
— One full bath
■ A long hallway dividing bedrooms and living areas assuring privacy
■ A centrally located utility room and bath
■ An open Living/Dining Room area with exposed beams, sloping ceilings and optional fireplace

FIRST FLOOR — 1,024 SQ. FT.
CARPORT & STORAGE — 387 SQ. FT.
DECK — 411 SQ. FT.

TOTAL LIVING AREA: 1,024 SQ. FT.

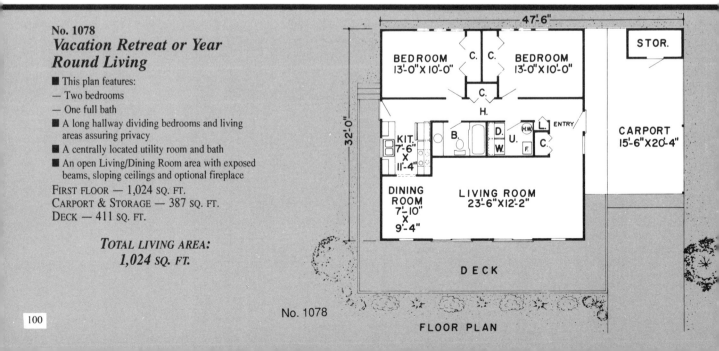

No. 1078

FLOOR PLAN

No. 84058
Well Planned Saltbox has Rustic Charm

■ This plan features:
— Three bedrooms
— Two full baths

■ Efficient use of living space creating a spacious feeling

■ A Living/Dining area occupying more than half of the lower level

■ A central chimney accommodating a built-in fireplace

■ An optional deck

■ An optional basement, slab or crawl space foundation available — please specify when ordering

FIRST FLOOR — 779 SQ. FT.
SECOND FLOOR — 519 SQ. FT.

TOTAL LIVING AREA:
1,298 SQ. FT.

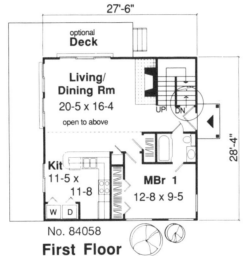

27'-6"

optional
Deck

Living/ Dining Rm
20-5 x 16-4

open to above

UP DN

28'-4"

Kit
11-5 x 11-8

MBr 1
12-8 x 9-5

W D

No. 84058
First Floor

opt. slab/crawl space

No materials list available

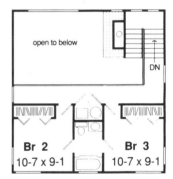

open to below

DN

Br 2
10-7 x 9-1

Br 3
10-7 x 9-1

Second Floor

No. 10445
Morning Room Accents

■ This plan features:
— Three bedrooms
— Two and one half baths
■ Tiled floors unifying the dining and food preparation areas
■ A Morning Room located off the well-organized Kitchen
■ A Family Room employing more tile accents which opens to the patio
■ A secluded Master Bedroom which includes a sunken tub, small greenhouses, and ample closet space

FIRST FLOOR — 2,466 SQ. FT.
GARAGE — 482 SQ. FT.

TOTAL LIVING AREA: 2,466 SQ. FT.

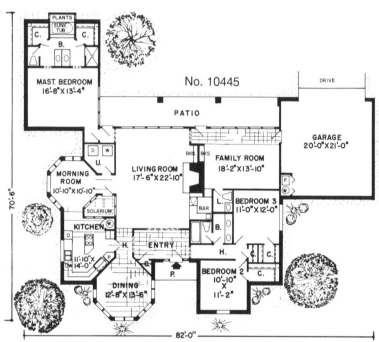

No. 20353
Window-Studded Brick Facade Communicates Success

■ This plan features:
— Three bedrooms
— Three full and one half bath
■ A sky-lit Foyer with a balcony above
■ A formal Dining Room made spacious by a vaulted ceiling
■ A large island Kitchen with peninsula counter that serves a glass-walled Breakfast area equipped with an adjoining pantry
■ A built-in bar in the huge Family Room with cozy fireplace that is just steps away from the elegant Parlor
■ A magnificent Master Suite with pan vault ceiling, fireplace, circular spa, two-way access to a private deck and large walk-in closet
■ Two additional bedrooms each with a full bath

FIRST FLOOR — 1,807 SQ. FT.
SECOND FLOOR — 1,359 SQ. FT.
BASEMENT — 1,807 SQ. FT.
GARAGE — 840 SQ. FT.

TOTAL LIVING AREA: 3,166 SQ. FT.

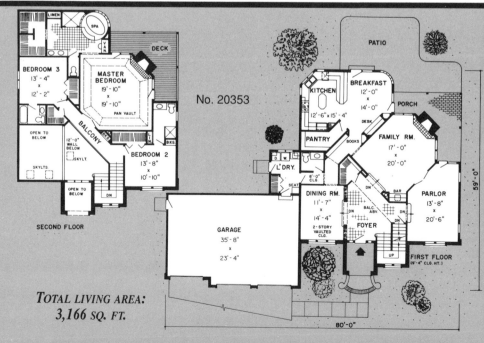

No. 9870
Master Bedroom Suite
Accentuates Luxury

■ This plan features:
— Three bedrooms
— Two and one half baths

■ A French Provincial design adorned with pillars and a bow window

■ The Kitchen centered between a laundry room and Kitchen Nook for added convenience

■ A spacious Family Room which opens to the terrace

■ A Master Bedroom complete with a full bath and sitting room placed to allow full privacy

FIRST FLOOR — 2,015 SQ. FT.
BASEMENT — 2,015 SQ. FT.
GARAGE — 545 SQ. FT.

TOTAL LIVING AREA:
2,015 SQ. FT.

MAIN AREA
No. 9870

No. 90689
Formal Balance

■ This plan features:

— Three bedrooms

— Two full baths

■ A cathedral ceiling in the Living Room with a heat-circulating fireplace as the focal point

■ A bow window in the Dining Room that adds elegance as well as natural light

■ A well-equipped Kitchen that serves both the Dinette and the formal Dining Room efficiently

■ A Master Bedroom with three closets and a private Master Bath with sliding glass doors to the Master Deck with a hot tub

FIRST FLOOR — 1,374 SQ. FT.
MUDROOM/LAUNDRY — 102 SQ. FT.
BASEMENT — 1,361 SQ. FT.
GARAGE — 548 SQ. FT.

TOTAL LIVING AREA:
1,476 SQ. FT.

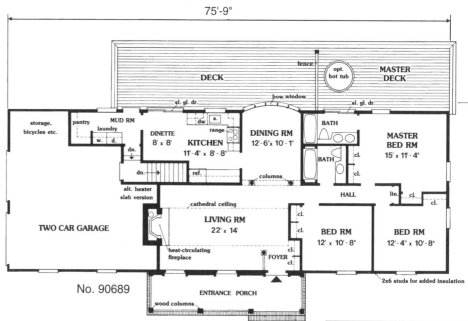

MAIN AREA

No. 24264
Warm and Inviting

■ This plan features:

— Four bedrooms

— Two full and one half bath

■ A see-through fireplace between the Living Room and the Family Room

■ A gourmet Kitchen with an island, a built-in pantry, and a double sink

■ A Master Bedroom with a vaulted ceiling

■ A Master Bath with large a double vanity, linen closet, a corner tub, a separate shower, a compartmented toilet, and huge walk-in closet

■ Three additional bedrooms, one with walk-in closet share full hall Bath

FIRST FLOOR — 1,241 SQ. FT.
SECOND FLOOR — 1,170 SQ. FT.

TOTAL LIVING AREA:
2,411 SQ. FT.

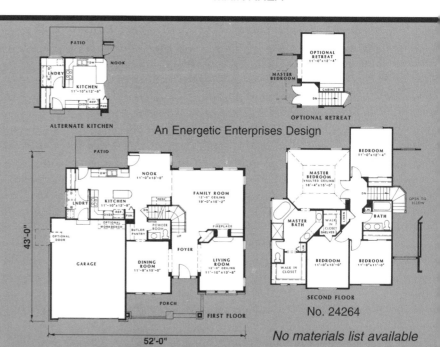

An Energetic Enterprises Design

No materials list available

No. 10380

Passive Solar Design with Unique Great Room

- This plan features:
- — Three bedrooms
- — Two and one half baths
- Exposed beams and large expanses of glass
- A six-sided living area
- Spiral stairs rising to a loft which overlooks the Great Room
- Rooms with sloping ceilings containing R-38 insulation
- Side walls containing R-24 insulation
- A full Basement foundation

FIRST FLOOR — 2,199 SQ. FT.
LOFT — 336 SQ. FT.
GARAGE — 611 SQ. FT.
BASEMENT — 2,199 SQ. FT.

TOTAL LIVING AREA:
2,535 SQ. FT.

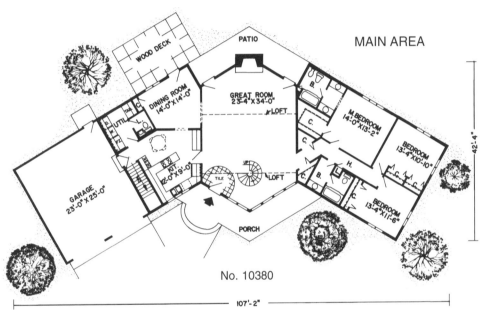

MAIN AREA

WOOD DECK

PATIO

DINING ROOM
14'-0" X 14'-0"

GREAT ROOM
23'-4" X 34'-0"

LOFT

M. BEDROOM
14'-0" X 13'-2"

UTIL

KIT
12'-0" X 9'-0"

TILE

UP

LOFT

BEDROOM
13'-4" X 10'-10"

GARAGE
23'-0" X 25'-0"

BEDROOM
13'-4" X 11'-6"

PORCH

No. 10380

42'-4"

107'-2"

No. 10519
Plan Yields Lots of Living Space

■ This plan features:
— Three bedrooms
— Two and one half baths
■ Sloped ceilings and an open central stairway
■ An efficient, U-shaped Kitchen with easy access to the Dining Room and a laundry facility
■ Ample closet space throughout the home

FIRST FLOOR — 872 SQ. FT.
SECOND FLOOR — 483 SQ. FT.

TOTAL LIVING AREA: 1,355 SQ. FT.

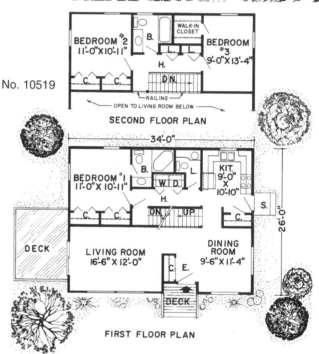

No. 9181
Roofed Walkway Attaches Garage

■ This plan features:
— Three bedrooms
— Two full and one half baths
■ An elegant Porch leads into an open Foyer and a spacious Living Room with a double fireplace and direct access to the formal Dining Room
■ A well-appointed Kitchen with a peninsula counter and adjacent to the formal Dining Room, the Family Room and the Utility area
■ An expansive Family Room with a double fireplace and a wood bin, as well as direct access to the Terrace
■ A corner Master Bedroom with an oversized closet and a private bath
■ Two additional bedrooms sharing a full hall bath

MAIN FLOOR — 2,014 SQ. FT.
GARAGE — 576 SQ. FT.

TOTAL LIVING AREA: 2,014 SQ. FT.

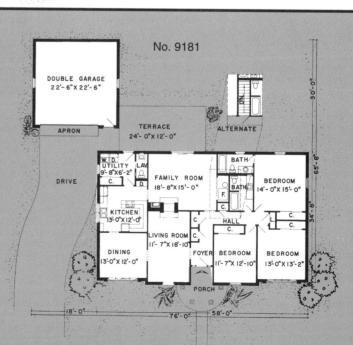

No. 10138
Perfect Lake Shore Home

◼ This plan features:
— Four bedrooms
— Two full and one half baths
◼ A large, wrap-a-round Deck providing easy, outdoor living
◼ A combination Living Room/Dining Room offers lovely views through two sliding glass doors
◼ An centrally located Kitchen serves the Dining area through folding doors and features a convenient laundry area
◼ Two roomy bedrooms with ample closet space with a one and a half bath arrangement
◼ An over-sized lower level Family Room with sliding glass doors to a Patio and two additional bedrooms sharing a full hall bath

UPPER LEVEL — 1,196 SQ. FT.
LOWER LEVEL — 1,196 SQ. FT.

TOTAL LIVING AREA:
2,392 SQ. FT.

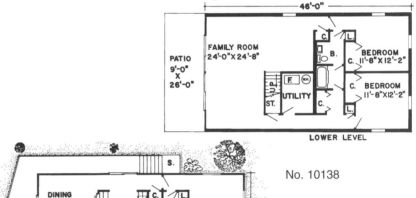

No. 10138

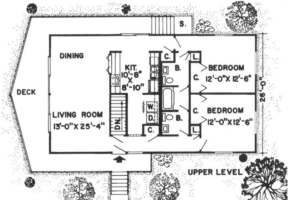

No. 24563
Classic Front Porch

■ This plan features:
— Four bedrooms
— Two full and one half baths
■ Stone and columns accenting the wrap-around front porch
■ A formal Living Room and Dining Room adjoining with columns at their entrances
■ An island Kitchen with a double sink, plenty of cabinet and counter space and a walk-in pantry
■ A Breakfast Room flowing into the Family Room and the Kitchen
■ A corner fireplace and a built-in entertainment center in the Family Room
■ A lavish Master Suite topped by a decorative ceiling and an ultra bath
■ Three roomy, additional bedrooms sharing a full hall bath

FIRST FLOOR — 1,584 SQ. FT.
SECOND FLOOR — 1,277 SQ. FT.
GARAGE — 550 SQ. FT.
BASEMENT — 1,584 SQ. FT.

TOTAL LIVING AREA:
2,861 SQ. FT.

A Britt J. Willis Design

First Floor

- Family Rm 16-0 x 17-1
- Brkfst 13-1 x 11-0 approx.
- Kitchen
- island snack bar
- Garage 24-8 x 21-8
- Dining Rm 11-8 x 11-0
- Foyer
- Living Rm 13-1 x 13-0
- Ldry
- 68'-0"
- 53'-0"
- Alternate Foundation Option
- crawl access

Second Floor No. 24563

- Master Suite 14-3 x 12-6 approx.
- Br 2 11-8 x 12-0
- Br 4 13-0 x 10-0 approx.
- Br 3 13-0 x 11-9

No materials list available

No. 90121
Glass Captures Views & Sun in A-Frame

■ This plan features:
— Three bedrooms
— Two full baths
■ Large exterior exposed beams
■ A Family Room with sliders to the deck
■ Wooden seats railing the deck which flows into a dining patio on the left side
■ A Master Bedroom including a large fireplaced sitting area
■ An optional basement, slab or crawl space foundation — please specify when ordering

FIRST FLOOR — 1,126 SQ. FT.
SECOND FLOOR — 624 SQ. FT.
BASEMENT — 1,100 SQ. FT.

TOTAL LIVING AREA:
1,750 SQ. FT.

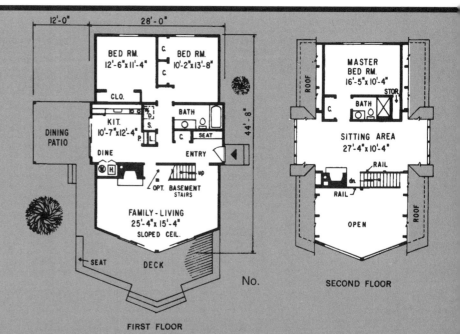

FIRST FLOOR

- 12'-0"
- 28'-0"
- 44'-8"
- BED RM. 12'-6" x 11'-4"
- BED RM. 10'-2" x 13'-8"
- CLO.
- KIT. 10'-7" x 12'-4"
- BATH
- DINING PATIO
- DINE
- ENTRY
- OPT. BASEMENT STAIRS
- FAMILY - LIVING 25'-4" x 15'-4" SLOPED CEIL.
- SEAT
- DECK

SECOND FLOOR

- MASTER BED RM. 16'-5" x 10'-4"
- BATH
- STOR.
- ROOF
- SITTING AREA 27'-4" x 10'-4"
- RAIL
- OPEN

No.

No. 84040

Unique Open Quality in Every Room

■ This plan features:

— Three bedrooms

— Two full and one half baths

■ Angular windows and recessed ceilings, separating the island Kitchen from the formal Dining and Breakfast Rooms

■ Twelve foot ceilings in the soaring, sky-lit Living Room

■ A Master Suite enhanced by bump-out windows, a personal bath, and a huge, walk-in closet

■ An optional slab, crawl space or basement foundation available, please specify when ordering

MAIN AREA — 2,026 SQ. FT.

GARAGE — 545 SQ. FT.

TOTAL LIVING AREA: 2,026 SQ. FT.

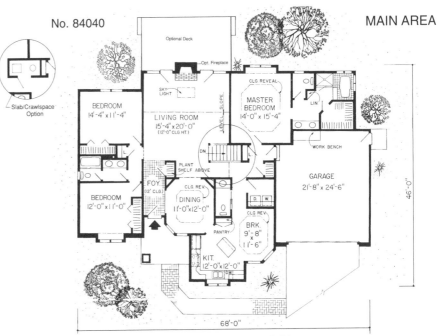

No. 84040

MAIN AREA

Slab/Crawlspace Option

BEDROOM 14'-4" x 11'-4"

Optional Deck

Opt. Fireplace

SKY-LIGHT

LIVING ROOM 15'-4" x 20'-0" (12'-0" CLG HT)

CLG REVEAL

MASTER BEDROOM 14'-0" x 15'-4"

LIN

WORK BENCH

DN

PLANT SHELF ABOVE

FOY (12' CLG)

BEDROOM 12'-0" x 11'-0"

CLG REV.

DINING 11'-0"x12'-0"

GARAGE 21'-8" x 24'-6"

D W

CLG REV

PANTRY

BRK 9'-8" x 11'-6"

KIT. 12'-0"x12'-0"

46'-0"

68'-0"

No materials list available

No. 90691
Classic Features

■ This plan features:
— Three bedrooms
— Two full baths
■ A cathedral ceiling in the Living Room with a heat-circulating fireplace
■ A spectacular bow window and skylight in the Dining Room
■ A sliding glass door and skylight in the Kitchen
■ A Master Bedroom including a private Master Bath with a whirlpool tub
■ Two additional bedrooms that share a full, double-vanity hall bath

MAIN AREA— 1,530 SQ. FT.
BASEMENT — 1,434 SQ. FT.

TOTAL LIVING AREA: 1,530 SQ. FT.

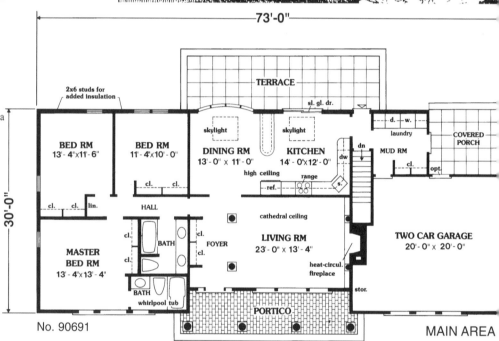

73'-0"

30'-0"

2x6 studs for added insulation

TERRACE

sl. gl. dr.

skylight   skylight

BED RM
13'-4"x11'-6"

BED RM
11'-4"x10'-0"

DINING RM
13'-0" x 11'-0"

KITCHEN
14'-0"x12'-0"

d. — w.

laundry

COVERED PORCH

dn

MUD RM

cl.

opt.

high ceiling

ref.   range

dw

s.

cl.   cl.

cl.   cl.   lin.

HALL

cl.

cl.

cathedral ceiling

BATH

FOYER

LIVING RM
23'-0" x 13'-4"

MASTER BED RM
13'-4"x13'-4"

TWO CAR GARAGE
20'-0" x 20'-0"

heat-circul. fireplace

stor.

BATH

whirlpool tub

PORTICO

No. 90691

MAIN AREA

No. 91031
Snug Retreat With A View

■ This plan features:
— One bedroom plus loft
— One full bath
■ A large front Deck providing views and an expansive entrance
■ A two-story Living/Dining area with double glass doors leading out to the Deck
■ An efficient, U-shaped Kitchen with a pass through counter to the Dining area
■ A first floor Bedroom, with ample closet space, located near a full shower bath
■ A Loft/Bedroom on the second floor offering multiple uses
■ This plan is available with a crawlspace foundation only.

MAIN FLOOR — 572 SQ. FT.
LOFT — 308 SQ. FT.

TOTAL LIVING AREA: 880 SQ. FT.

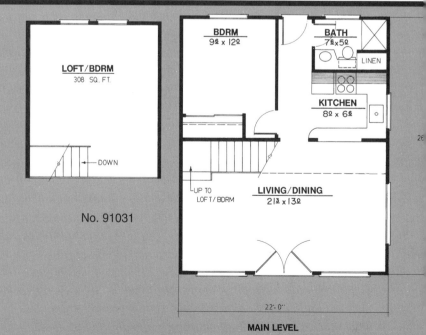

LOFT/BDRM
308 SQ. FT.

DOWN

BDRM
9⁰ x 12⁰

BATH
7⁰ x 5⁰

LINEN

KITCHEN
8⁰ x 6⁰

No. 91031

UP TO LOFT/BDRM

LIVING/DINING
21⁰ x 13⁰

22'-0"

MAIN LEVEL

No. 91700
Country Style For Today

■ This plan features:
— Three bedrooms
— Two full and one half baths

■ A wide wrap-around porch for a farm-house style

■ A spacious Living Room with double doors and a large front window

■ A garden window over the double sink in the huge, country Kitchen with two islands, one a butcher block, and the other an eating bar

■ A corner fireplace in the Family Room enjoyed throughout the Nook and Kitchen, thanks to an open layout

■ A Master Suite with a spa tub, and a huge walk-in closet as well as a shower and double vanities

FIRST FLOOR — 1,785 SQ. FT.
SECOND FLOOR — 621 SQ. FT.

TOTAL LIVING AREA:
2,406 SQ. FT.

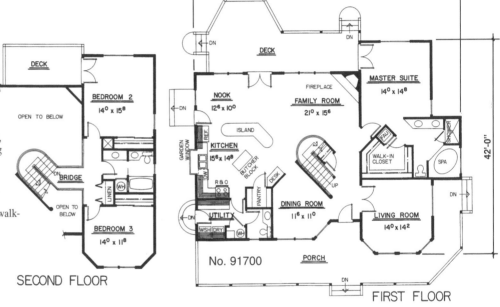

SECOND FLOOR

FIRST FLOOR

No. 91700

No. 20303

Good Things Come in Small Packages

■ This plan features:
— Three bedrooms
— Two full baths

■ An air-lock vestibule entry that keeps the chill outside

■ A cozy sitting nook in the Living Room

■ A well-equipped Kitchen with a Breakfast nook

■ A sky-lit hall bath shared by two of the bedrooms

■ A Master Suite with his-n-her closets and a private, sky-lit full bath

FIRST FLOOR — 885 SQ. FT.
SECOND FLOOR — 368 SQ. FT.
BASEMENT — 715 SQ. FT.

TOTAL LIVING AREA: 1,253 SQ. FT.

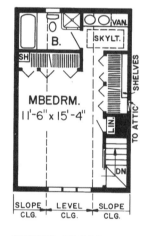

SECOND FLOOR

No. 20303

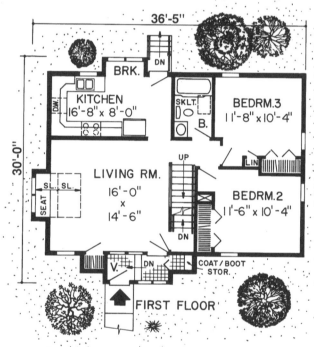

No. 34851

Traditional Gem

■ This plan features:
— Three bedrooms
— Two full and one half baths

■ A sloped-ceiling Living/Dining Room combination

■ A Family Room with a fireplace

■ A Kitchen with a built-in pantry

■ A Master Suite with a sloped ceiling, and a private Master Bath

■ Two additional bedrooms with direct access to a full bath

FIRST FLOOR — 1,056 SQ. FT.
SECOND FLOOR — 874 SQ. FT.
BASEMENT — 1,023 SQ. FT.
GARAGE — 430 SQ. FT.

TOTAL LIVING AREA: 1,930 SQ. FT.

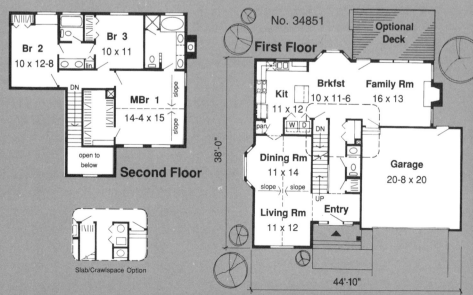

Slab/Crawlspace Option

No. 20203
Contemporary with a Country Flair

■ This plan features:
— Three bedrooms
— Two and a half baths
■ A fireplaced Living Room flowing easily into the Dining Room which boasts a decorative ceiling
■ A Master Suite with a walk-in closet and a private Master Bath
■ Two additional bedrooms sharing a full sky-lit bath

FIRST FLOOR — 1,229 SQ. FT.
SECOND FLOOR — 515 SQ. FT.
GARAGE — 452 SQ. FT.

TOTAL LIVING AREA: 1,744 SQ. FT.

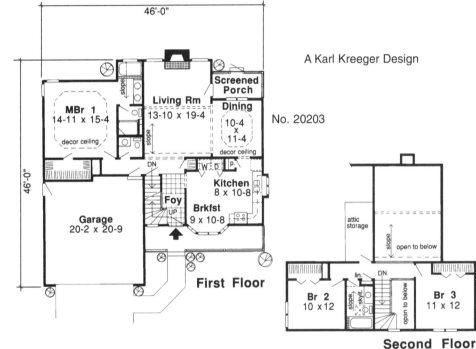

A Karl Kreeger Design

No. 20203

First Floor

Second Floor

No. 90109
Attractive Fieldstone and Vertical Siding

■ This plan features:
— Four bedrooms
— Two full baths

■ Double door entry framed with glass leads into the formal Living Room with a sloped ceiling

■ Convenient Family Room with a sliding glass door to the Patio

■ L-shaped Kitchen with a peninsula counter/eating bar hub for the Breakfast area, Family Room, Dining and Utility areas

■ Master Bedroom suite enhanced by a walk-in closet, a private bath and an optional Den access

■ Three additional bedrooms share a double vanity bath

■ This plan is available with a Basement or Crawlspace foundation. Please specify when ordering

MAIN FLOOR — 2,305 SQ. FT.
GARAGE — 530 SQ. FT.

TOTAL LIVING AREA:
2,305 SQ. FT.

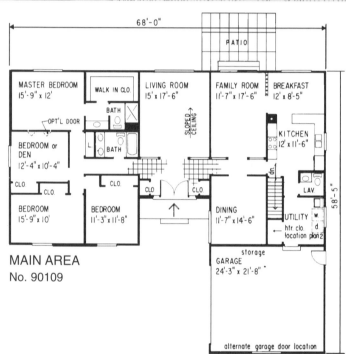

MAIN AREA
No. 90109

No. 24588
Plenty of Room Inside

A Britt J. Willis Design

■ This plan features:
— Three bedrooms
— Two full baths

■ Impressive entrance with a transom window leads into the open Foyer and Great Room

■ Central Great Room with a fireplace and a vaulted ceiling accented by columns

■ Large Kitchen with a work island opens to an Dining area with a walk-in pantry, a built-in desk and French doors to the Screen Porch

■ Convenient Garage entrance and laundry adjacent to the Kitchen

■ Master Suite with a vaulted ceiling above a triple window, a walk-in closet and a private bath

■ This plan is available with a Basement foundation only

MAIN FLOOR — 2,504 SQ. FT.
BASEMENT — 1,044 SQ. FT.
GARAGE — 724 SQ. FT.

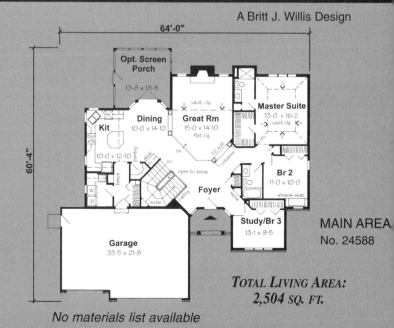

MAIN AREA
No. 24588

TOTAL LIVING AREA:
2,504 SQ. FT.

No materials list available

No. 84083
Separate Studio with a View

■ This plan features:
— Three bedrooms
— Two full baths

■ A spacious Foyer leading into a Living/Dining Room area with vaulted ceilings, a wall of windows, a stone fireplace and built-in shelves

■ A galley-styled Kitchen opening into the Breakfast area and the Family Room while adjacent to the Dining Room and the Garage

■ A two-story Family Room offering built-in cabinets and access to the rear Deck or Patio

■ A private Master Bedroom suite featuring a private bath and two closets

■ Two additional bedrooms share a full hall bath

■ A second floor Studio offering a wall of windows and a view of the Family Room below

FIRST FLOOR — 2,238 SQ. FT.
SECOND FLOOR — 284 SQ. FT.
GARAGE — 480 SQ. FT.

TOTAL LIVING AREA:
2,522 SQ. FT.

No materials list available

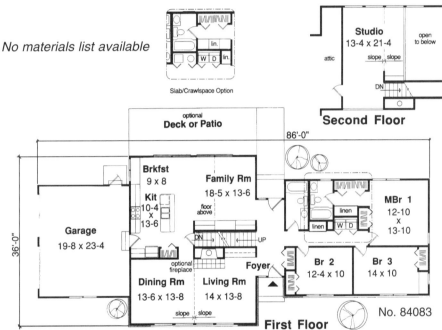

Slab/Crawlspace Option

Second Floor

Studio
13-4 x 21-4

attic   slope | slope   open to below

DN

86'-0"

optional
Deck or Patio

Brkfst
9 x 8

Family Rm
18-5 x 13-6

Kit
10-4 x 13-6

floor above

36'-0"

Garage
19-8 x 23-4

optional fireplace

DN   UP

MBr 1
12-10 x 13-10

linen

linen   W D

Br 2
12-4 x 10

Br 3
14 x 10

Dining Rm
13-6 x 13-8

Living Rm
14 x 13-8

Foyer

slope | slope

First Floor

No. 84083

No. 10677
Arches Grace Classic Facade

■ This plan features:
— Three bedrooms
— Two and one half baths
■ Built-in planters and half walls to define rooms
■ A balcony that connects three upstairs bedrooms
■ Double sinks and built-in vanities in the Master Bath
■ Ample closet space

FIRST FLOOR — 932 SQ. FT.
SECOND FLOOR — 764 SQ. FT.
GARAGE — 430 SQ. FT.
BASEMENT — 920 SQ. FT.

TOTAL LIVING AREA:
1,696 SQ. FT.

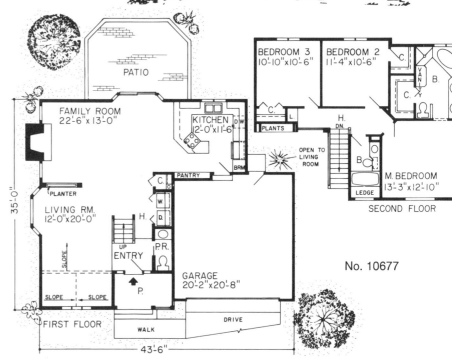

No. 20070
Sheltered Porch is an Inviting Entrance

■ This plan features:
— Three bedrooms
— Two and one half baths
■ A dramatic two-story entry
■ A fireplaced Living Room
■ A modern Kitchen flowing easily into a sunny Breakfast Nook
■ A formal Dining Room with elegant decorative ceiling
■ A Master Bedroom highlighted by a sky lit bath

FIRST FLOOR — 877 SQ. FT.
SECOND FLOOR — 910 SQ. FT.
BASEMENT — 877 SQ. FT.
GARAGE — 458 SQ. FT.

TOTAL LIVING AREA:
1,787 SQ. FT.

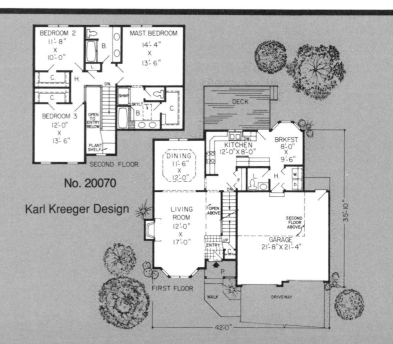

No. 20070

Karl Kreeger Design

No. 24259

Attractive Combination of Brick and Siding

■ This plan features:
— Three Bedrooms
— Two full Baths

■ A Great Room sunny bayed area, fireplace and built-in entertainment center

■ A private Master Bedroom with luxurious Master Bath and walk-in closet

■ Dining Room has a Butler Pantry

■ Two additional Bedrooms have use of hall full Bath

MAIN AREA — 2,010 SQ. FT.

TOTAL LIVING AREA: 2,010 SQ. FT.

An Energetic Enterprises Design

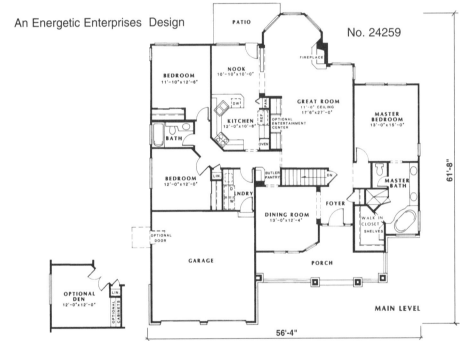

No. 24259

PATIO

BEDROOM
11'-10"x12'-6"

NOOK
10'-10"x10'-0"

FIREPLACE

GREAT ROOM
11'-0" CEILING
17'6"x27'-0"

MASTER BEDROOM
13'-0"x15'-0"

KITCHEN
12'-0"x10'-8"

OPTIONAL ENTERTAINMENT CENTER

BATH

OVEN

BEDROOM
12'-0"x12'-0"

LIN

LNDRY

BUTLER PANTRY

DN

MASTER BATH

DINING ROOM
13'-0"x12'-4"

FOYER

WALK IN CLOSET

SHELVES

OPTIONAL DOOR

GARAGE

PORCH

61'-8"

MAIN LEVEL

OPTIONAL DEN
12'-0"x12'-0"

LIN

OPTIONAL CABINETS

56'-4"

No. 20075
Compact and Appealing

■ This plan features:
— Three bedrooms
— Two full baths

■ A fireplaced Living Room and formal Dining Room with extra wide doorways

■ A centrally located Kitchen for maximum convenience

■ A Master Bedroom with vaulted ceiling and private Master Bath and walk-in closet

FIRST FLOOR — 1,682 SQ. FT.
BASEMENT — 1,682 SQ. FT.
GARAGE — 484 SQ. FT.

TOTAL LIVING AREA:
1,682 SQ. FT.

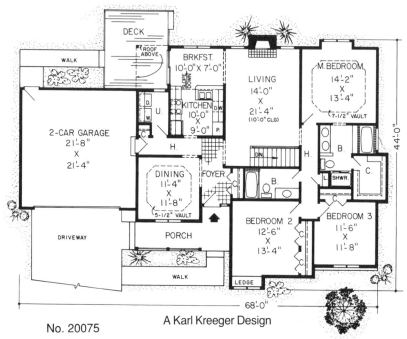

No. 20075

A Karl Kreeger Design

No. 20100
Wide Open and Convenient

A Karl Kreeger Design

■ This plan features:
— Three bedrooms
— Two full baths

■ Vaulted ceilings in the Dining Room and Master Bedroom

■ A sloped ceiling in the fireplaced Living Room

■ A skylight illuminating the Master Bath

■ A large Master Bedroom with walk-in closet

FIRST FLOOR — 1,727 SQ. FT.
BASEMENT — 1,727 SQ. FT.
GARAGE — 484 SQ. FT.

TOTAL LIVING AREA:
1,727 SQ. FT.

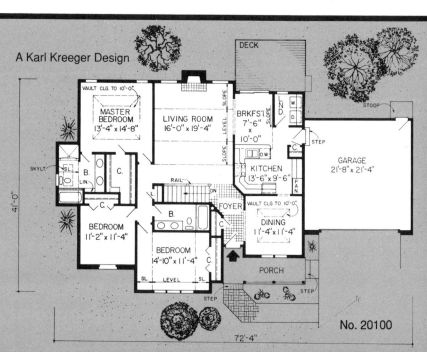

No. 20100

No. 90123
Old American Saltbox Design

■ This plan features:
— Three bedrooms
— One and one half baths
■ A sloping Living Room ceiling that lends to spaciousness
■ A centrally located fireplace
■ Laundry facilities conveniently located off Kitchen area
■ A slab foundation only

FIRST FLOOR — 811 SQ. FT.
SECOND FLOOR — 488 SQ. FT.

TOTAL LIVING AREA:
1,299 SQ. FT.

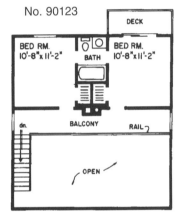

No. 90123

DECK

BED RM.
10'-8"x11'-2"

BATH

BED RM.
10'-8"x11'-2"

dn.

BALCONY

RAIL

OPEN

SECOND FLOOR

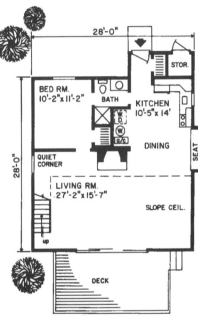

28'-0"

STOR.

BED RM.
10'-2"x11'-2"

BATH

KITCHEN
10'-5"x 14'

28'-0"

W.D.

W

G/E

DINING

SEAT

QUIET
CORNER

LIVING RM.
27'-2"x15'-7"

SLOPE CEIL.

up

DECK

FIRST FLOOR

No. 24316
First Floor Master Suite

■ This plan features:
— Four bedrooms
— Two full and one half baths

■ A formal Living Room, with a distinctive boxed window, stepping down from an open Foyer and formal Dining Room

■ A bright, efficient Kitchen with a corner double sink, a bay window area for informal eating and open access to the Family Room and Patio

■ Unique corner fireplace in the Family Room serving as a cozy focal point

■ A first floor Master Suite featuring a double closet and a private Bath with a double vanity and a raised window tub

■ Three additional bedrooms on the second floor sharing a full hall bath

FIRST FLOOR — 1,400 SQ. FT.
SECOND FLOOR — 540 SQ. FT.

TOTAL LIVING AREA:
1,940 SQ. FT.

No. 24316

Second Floor

A Don Marshall Design

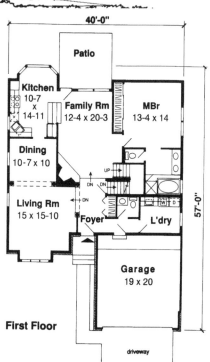

First Floor

No. 10839
Perfect Compact Ranch

■ This plan features:
— Two bedrooms
— Two full baths

■ A large, sunken Great Room with a cozy fireplace

■ A Master Bedroom with an unforgettable skylit Bathroom

■ A three-car Garage, with a work area for the family carpenter

■ A Kitchen with a Breakfast Nook for family gatherings

FIRST FLOOR — 1,738 SQ. FT.
BASEMENT — 1,083 SQ. FT.
GARAGE — 796 SQ. FT.

TOTAL LIVING AREA:
1,738 SQ. FT.

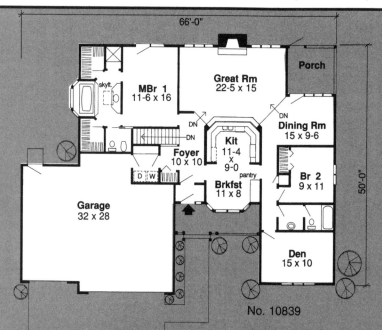

No. 10839

No. 24250
Smart, Spacious Design

■ This plan features:
— Three bedrooms
— Two full baths

■ Custom, volume ceilings

■ A sunken Living Room with a vaulted ceiling and a fireplace

■ A center island and an eating nook in the Kitchen

■ A spacious Master Suite that includes a vaulted ceiling and a lavish bath

■ Secondary bedrooms with custom ceiling treatments and use of a full hall bath

MAIN AREA — 1,700 SQ. FT.

TOTAL LIVING AREA: 1,700 SQ. FT.

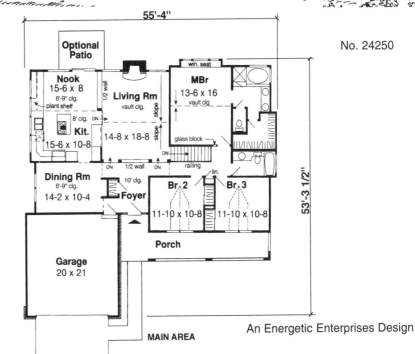

55'-4"

Optional Patio

Nook
15-6 x 8
8'-9" clg.
plant shelf

Living Rm
vault clg.

win. seat

MBr
13-6 x 16
vault clg

1/2 wall

8' clg.

Kit.
15-6 x 10-8

14-8 x 18-8

slope

slope

DN

glass block

DN

DN

1/2 wall

DN

railing

Dining Rm
8'-9" clg.
14-2 x 10-4

10' clg.

Foyer

Br. 2
11-10 x 10-8

lin.

Br. 3
11-10 x 10-8

Garage
20 x 21

Porch

53'-3 1/2"

No. 24250

An Energetic Enterprises Design

MAIN AREA

No. 24566
Classic and Classy Design

This plan features:

— Three or four bedrooms
— Two full and one half baths

- A gracious entrance into a bright Foyer with a landing staircase and convenient closet
- Formal Living and Dining rooms highlighted by bay windows
- A comfortable Family Room offers a fireplace and lots of windows
- An efficient Kitchen with a work island/snack-bar, walk-in pantry and adjacent Utility room entrance from Garage
- A private Master Bedroom suite offers a decorative window below a sloped ceiling, a large walk-in closet and plush bath with whirlpool tub
- Two additional bedrooms and an Office have ample closets and share a double vanity bath

FIRST FLOOR — 1,377 SQ. FT.
SECOND FLOOR — 1,264 SQ. FT.
BASEMENT — 1,316 SQ. FT.
GARAGE — 693 SQ. FT.
FOUNDATION — BASEMENT, SLAB OR CRAWL SPACE

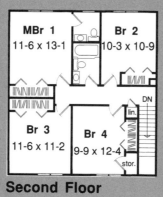

Second Floor
No. 24566

TOTAL LIVING AREA:
2,641 SQ. FT.

A Britt J. Willis Design

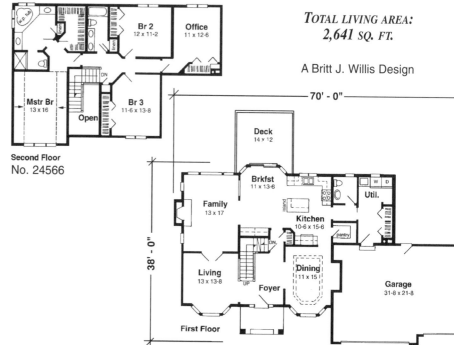

70' - 0"
38' - 0"

Deck
14 x 12

Brkfst
11 x 13-6

Util.

Family
13 x 17

Kitchen
10-6 x 15-6

pantry

Living
13 x 13-8

Dining
11 x 15

Foyer

Garage
31-8 x 21-8

First Floor

No. 84079
Traditional and Efficient Design

This plan features:

— Four bedrooms
— One full and two half baths

- A covered entrance into open Foyer with a landing staircase and formal Living Room with a decorative window
- A comfortable Family Room with a focal point fireplace and sliding glass door to back yard
- An efficient, U-shaped Kitchen easily serves formal Dining and Breakfast areas
- A corner Master Bedroom with private bath and double closet
- Three additional bedrooms with ample closets, share a full bath

FIRST FLOOR — 1,203 SQ. FT.
SECOND FLOOR — 828 SQ. FT.
GARAGE — 401 SQ. FT.
FOUNDATION — BASEMENT, SLAB OR CRAWL SPACE

MBr 1
11-6 x 13-1

Br 2
10-3 x 10-9

Br 3
11-6 x 11-2

Br 4
9-9 x 12-4

Second Floor

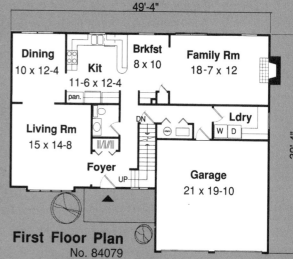

49'-4"
39'-4"

Dining
10 x 12-4

Kit
11-6 x 12-4

Brkfst
8 x 10

Family Rm
18-7 x 12

Living Rm
15 x 14-8

Ldry

Foyer

Garage
21 x 19-10

First Floor Plan
No. 84079

TOTAL LIVING AREA:
2,031 SQ. FT.

No materials list available

No. 20086
Gardener's Dream House

■ This plan features:
— Three bedrooms
— Two full baths
■ Unlimited opportunities for entry gardening
■ A vaulted ceiling in the Living Room and Dining Room
■ An island Kitchen with a Breakfast area
■ A Master Bedroom with a sky-lit Master Bath and a walk-in closet

MAIN AREA — 1,628 SQ. FT.
BASEMENT — 1,628 SQ. FT.
GARAGE — 434 SQ. FT.

TOTAL LIVING AREA:
1,628 SQ. FT.

A Karl Kreeger Design

52'-6"

M. BEDROOM
15'-6"X11'-4"

VAULT CLG.

DINING
11'-0"X9'-4"

DECK

SKY LT.

C.
DRESS.

B.
SHWR.
B.

LIVING
15'-0"X21'-4"

P.

ISLAND

DW

DESK

KIT./BRKFST.
13'-0"X17'-6"

H.

C.

BEDROOM 3
10'-8"X11'-0"

FOYER

C.

DOWN

C.

U.   D.
W.

BEDROOM 2
11'-2"X11'-2"

C.

P.

56'-4"

No. 20086

WALK

GARAGE
20'-4"X21'-6"

DRIVE

MAIN AREA

No. 90685
Farmhouse Flavor

■ This plan features:
— Three bedrooms
— Two full baths

■ An octagonal stair tower

■ A Foyer opening to a Living and Dining Room combination, enhanced by a striking glass wall

■ A heat circulating fireplace adding welcome warmth

■ A galley-style Kitchen including a large pantry, snack bar, and laundry area

■ A Master Suite with a private deck overlooking the backyard

First Floor — 1,073 sq. ft.
Second Floor — 604 sq. ft.
Retreat Tower — 93 sq. ft.
Garage — 428 sq. ft.

TOTAL LIVING AREA:
1,770 sq. ft.

No. 90685

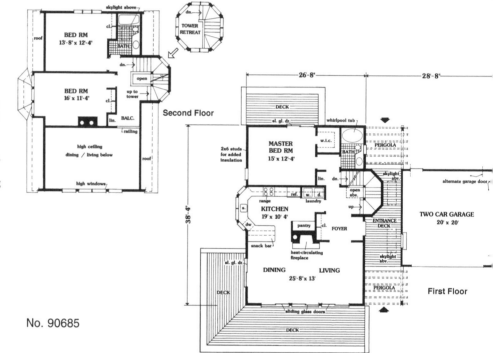

Second Floor

First Floor

No. 34029
Skylight Brightens Master Bedroom

■ This plan features:
— Three bedrooms
— Two full baths

■ A covered-porch entry

■ A foyer separating the Dining Room from the Breakfast area and Kitchen

■ A Living Room enhanced by a vaulted beam ceiling and a fireplace

■ A Master Bedroom with a decorative ceiling and a skylight in the private bath

■ An optional deck accessible through sliding doors off the Master Bedroom

First Floor — 1,698 sq. ft.
Garage — 484 sq. ft.

TOTAL LIVING AREA:
1,698 sq. ft.

MAIN AREA

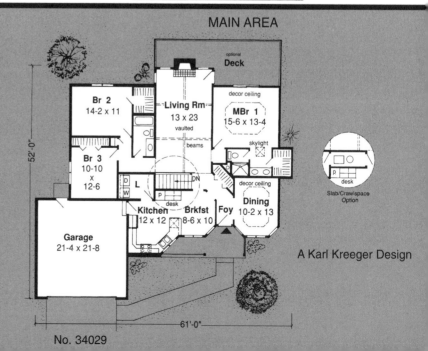

A Karl Kreeger Design

No. 34029

No. 20111
High Impact Family Home

■ This plan features:

— Four bedrooms

— Two and one half baths

■ A balcony linking the upstairs bedrooms and a skylit bath dividing a two-story foyer

■ A massive fireplace in the open Living Room

■ A well-situated Kitchen handy to both the formal Dining Room and sunny Breakfast area

■ A convenient, private first-floor Master Suite with a garden tub, step-in shower, and walk-in closet

FIRST FLOOR — 1,680 SQ. FT.

SECOND FLOOR — 514 SQ. FT.

BASEMENT — 1,045 SQ. FT.

GARAGE — 635 SQ. FT.

TOTAL LIVING AREA:
2,194 SQ. FT.

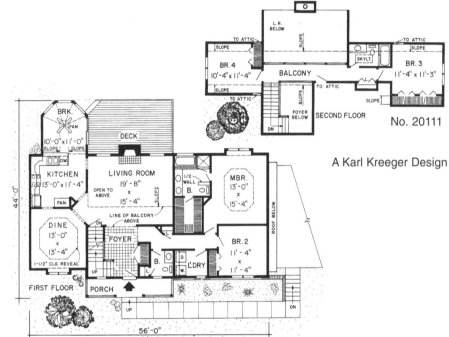

No. 20111

A Karl Kreeger Design

No. 10274
Fireplace Center of Circular Living Area

■ This plan features:

— Three bedrooms

— Two full baths

■ A dramatically positioned fireplace as a focal point for the main living area

■ The Kitchen, Dining and Living Rooms form a circle that allows work areas to flow into living areas

■ Sliding glass doors accessible to wood a Deck

■ A convenient Laundry Room located off the Kitchen

■ A double Garage providing excellent storage

MAIN AREA— 1,783 SQ. FT.

GARAGE — 576 SQ. FT.

TOTAL LIVING AREA: 1,783 SQ. FT.

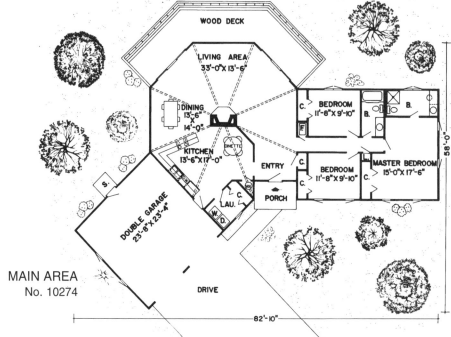

MAIN AREA
No. 10274

No. 24262
Attractive Hip and Valley Style Roof

An Energetic Enterprises Design

■ This plan features:

— Four bedrooms

— Two full and one half bath

■ A see-through fireplace between the Living Room and the Family Room

■ A gourmet Kitchen with an island, built-in pantry, and double sink

■ A Master Bedroom with a vaulted ceiling

■ A Master Bath with large double vanity, linen closet, corner tub, separate shower, compartmented toilet, and huge walk-in closet

■ Three additional bedrooms, one with walk-in closet share full hall Bath

FIRST FLOOR — 1,241 SQ. FT.

SECOND FLOOR — 1,170 SQ. FT.

TOTAL LIVING AREA: 2,411 SQ. FT.

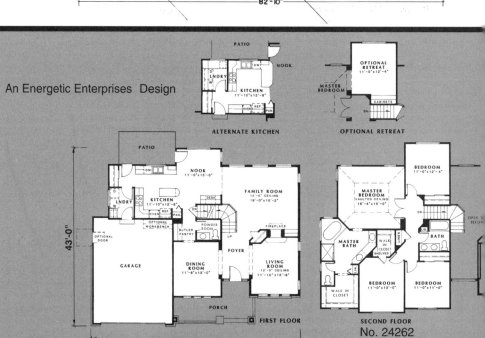

No. 24262

126

No. 10581

Corner Fireplace Warms Living Room

■ This plan features:
— Four bedrooms
— Three baths

■ A Parlor, Formal Dining Room, Kitchen, Breakfast Room and Living Room revolving around a central staircase

■ A Laundry room located near two bedrooms for convenience

■ A screened porch and deck which can be accessed from the large Living Room or the spacious Kitchen area

FIRST FLOOR — 1,916 SQ. FT.
SECOND FLOOR — 740 SQ. FT.
BASEMENT — 1,916 SQ. FT.
GARAGE — 814 SQ. FT.
SCREENED PORCH — 192 SQ. FT.

TOTAL LIVING AREA: 2,656 SQ. FT.

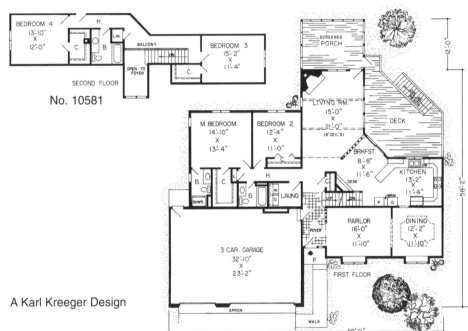

No. 10581

A Karl Kreeger Design

No. 10534
Private Court with Hot Tub Outside Master Bedroom

■ This plan features:
— Four bedrooms
— Three and one half baths
■ A private court adjoining the Master Suite which includes a hot tub
■ A cozy Library which opens onto the two-story foyer through French doors
■ A Morning Room with built-ins, a bar with wine storage, and a sun porch

FIRST FLOOR — 2,486 SQ. FT.
SECOND FLOOR — 954 SQ. FT.
BASEMENT — 2,486 SQ. FT.
GARAGE — 576 SQ. FT.

**TOTAL LIVING AREA:
3,440 SQ. FT.**

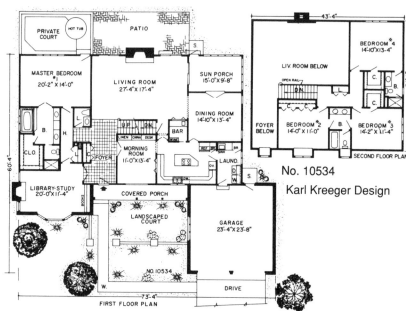

No. 10534   Karl Kreeger Design

FIRST FLOOR PLAN

No. 34049
Tower Stimulates Interest

■ This plan features:
— Four bedrooms
— Three full baths
■ Sloping ceilings and lofty open spaces
■ A rustic, fireplaced Living Room with sloped ceilings to enhance the atmosphere
■ A Master Suite with vaulted ceilings, walk-in closet, dressing area and Master Bath
■ Two upstairs bedrooms sharing a full bath

FIRST FLOOR — 1,496 SQ. FT.
SECOND FLOOR — 520 SQ. FT.
GARAGE — 424 SQ. FT.

**TOTAL LIVING AREA:
2,016 SQ. FT.**

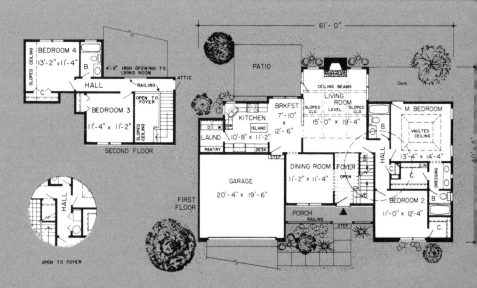

No. 34049   A Karl Kreeger Design

No. 10593
Victorian Details

■ This plan features:

— Four bedrooms

— Two and one half baths

■ A large country Kitchen in full view of a breakfast area

■ A fireplace shared by the cozy Living Room and the Family Room containing a bar and access to the patio

■ Octagonal recessed ceilings in the formal Dining Room

■ Walk-in closets enhancing all the bedrooms

FIRST FLOOR — 1,450 SQ. FT.

SECOND FLOOR — 1,341 SQ. FT.

BASEMENT — 1,450 SQ. FT.

GARAGE — 629 SQ. FT.

COVERED PORCH — 144 SQ. FT.

WOOD STORAGE — 48 SQ. FT.

TOTAL LIVING AREA:
2,791 SQ. FT.

No. 10593

A Karl Kreeger Design

No. 10386
Modified Cape with Passive Solar Features

■ This plan features:
— Three bedrooms
— Two baths

■ A solar greenhouse on the south side of the home employing energy storage rods and water to capture the sun's warmth

■ Triple glazed windows for energy efficiency

■ A Living Room accentuated by a heat circulating fireplace

■ Sliding doors leading from the sitting area of the Master Bedroom to a private patio

■ A Garage with a large storage area

FIRST FLOOR — 1,164 SQ. FT.
SECOND FLOOR — 574 SQ. FT.
BASEMENT — 1,164 SQ. FT.
GARAGE & STORAGE AREA — 574 SQ. FT.
GREENHOUSE — 238 SQ. FT.

TOTAL LIVING AREA:
1,738 SQ. FT.

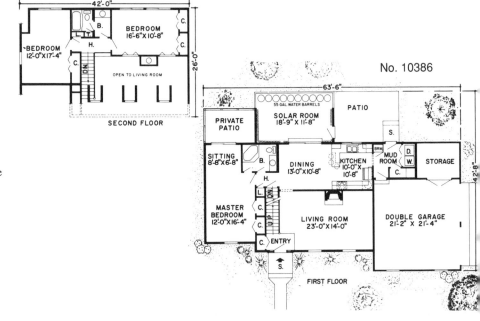

No. 10386

No. 20146
Family Favorite

■ This plan features:
— Three bedrooms
— Two full baths

■ A sky-lit breakfast bay

■ A Dining Room with recessed ceilings

■ A Master Suite featuring double vanitied bath and walk-in closet

FIRST FLOOR — 1,352 SQ. FT.
SECOND FLOOR — 736 SQ. FT.
BASEMENT — 1,340 SQ. FT.
GARAGE — 490 SQ. FT.

TOTAL LIVING AREA:
2,088 SQ. FT.

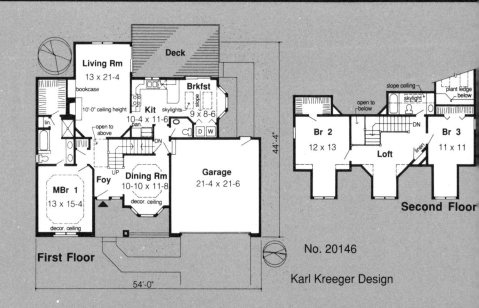

No. 20146

Karl Kreeger Design

No. 20205
Small But Room To Grow

■ This plan features:
— Three Bedrooms
— Two full Baths

■ A Master Suite with a vaulted ceiling and its own skylit Bath

■ A fireplaced Living Room with a sloped ceiling

■ Efficient Kitchen with a Breakfast Nook

■ Options for growth on the lower level

MAIN AREA — 1,321 SQ. FT.
LOWER LEVEL — 286 SQ. FT.
GARAGE — 655 SQ. FT.

TOTAL LIVING AREA:
1,607 SQ. FT.

Main Floor Plan
No. 20205

A Karl Kreeger Design

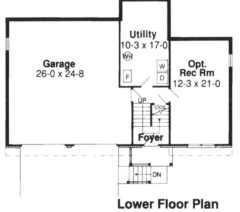

Lower Floor Plan

No. 10689
Elegant and Inviting

- This plan features:
— Five bedrooms
— Three and one half baths
- Wrap-around verandas and a three-season porch
- An elegant Parlor with a parquet floor and a formal Dining Room separated by a half-wall
- An adjoining Kitchen with a Breakfast bar and nook
- A Gathering Room with a fireplace, soaring ceilings and access to the porch

FIRST FLOOR — 1,580 SQ. FT.
SECOND FLOOR — 1,164 SQ. FT.
BASEMENT — 1,329 SQ. FT.
GARAGE — 576 SQ. FT.

**TOTAL LIVING AREA:
2,744 SQ. FT.**

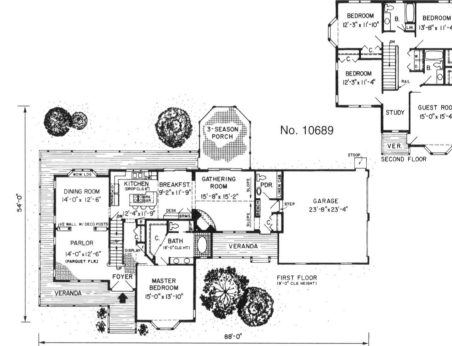

No. 10690
Gingerbread Charm

- This plan features:
— Three bedrooms
— Two and one half baths
- A wrap-around porch and rear deck adding lots of extra living space
- A formal Parlor and Dining Room just off the central entry
- A Family Room with a fireplace
- A Master Suite complete with a five-sided sitting nook, walk-in closets and a sunken tub

FIRST FLOOR — 1,260 SQ. FT.
SECOND FLOOR — 1,021 SQ. FT.
BASEMENT — 1,186 SQ. FT.
GARAGE — 840 SQ. FT.

**TOTAL LIVING AREA:
2,281 SQ. FT.**

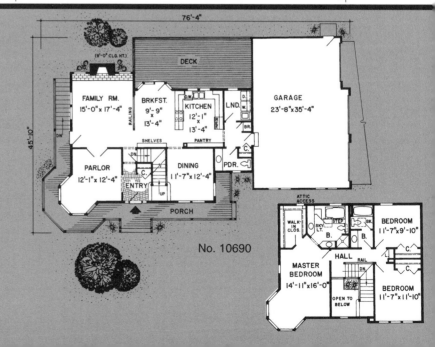

No. 24610
Second Floor Balcony Overlooks Great Room

■ This plan features:
— Three bedrooms
— Two full and one half baths

■ A Great Room with a focal point fireplace and a two story ceiling

■ An efficient Kitchen with an island, double sinks, built-in pantry and ample storage and counter space

■ A convenient first floor Laundry Room

■ A Dining Room with easy access to both the Kitchen and the outside

■ A Master Suite with a private master Bath and a walk-in closet

■ Two additional bedrooms with ample closet space that share a full hall bath

FIRST FLOOR — 891 SQ. FT.
SECOND FLOOR — 894 SQ. FT.
GARAGE — 534 SQ. FT.
BASEMENT — 891 SQ. FT.

TOTAL LIVING AREA:
1,785 SQ. FT.

A Greg Stafford Design

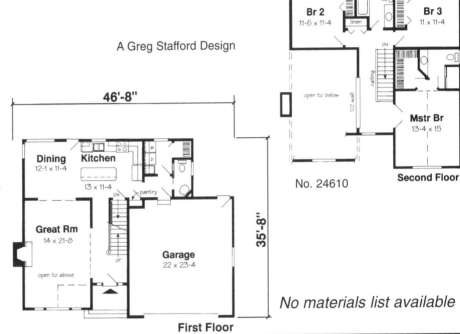

No. 24610

No materials list available

No. 20066
Cathedral Window Graced by Massive Arch

■ This plan features:
— Three bedrooms
— Two full baths

■ A tiled threshold providing a distinctive entrance

■ A comfortable Living Room with a wood-burning fireplace and tiled hearth

■ A Dining Room with vaulted ceiling

■ A Kitchen with central work island, pantry, planning desk, and Breakfast area

■ A Master Suite with decorative ceilings, Master Bath and bow window

FIRST FLOOR — 1,850 SQ. FT.
BASEMENT — 1,850 SQ. FT.
GARAGE — 503 SQ. FT.

TOTAL LIVING AREA:
1,850 SQ. FT.

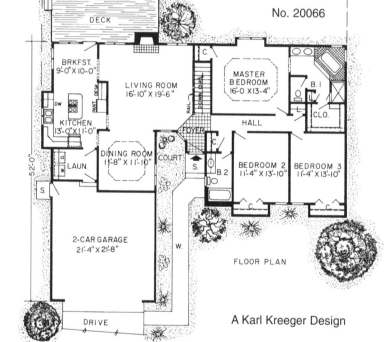

No. 20066

DECK

63'-8"

BRKFST.
9'-0" X 10'-0"

LIVING ROOM
16'-10" X 19'-6"

MASTER
BEDROOM
16'-0 X13'-4"

B.1

KITCHEN
13'-0" X 11'-0"

CLO.

HALL

52'-0"

DINING ROOM
11'-8" X 11'-10"

FOYER

COURT

BEDROOM 2
11'-4" X 13'-10"

BEDROOM 3
11'-4" X 13'-10"

B.2

LAUN.

2-CAR GARAGE
21'-4" X 21'-8"

W.

FLOOR PLAN

DRIVE

A Karl Kreeger Design

No. 9828
Superior Comfort and Privacy

■ This plan features:
— Four bedrooms
— Three full baths

■ A natural stone exterior with slate floors in the Foyer and leading to the private patio off the Master Bedroom

■ A two-way fireplace between the Living Room and Family Room

■ A Breakfast Nook with a large bow window facing the terrace and pool

■ Four bedrooms grouped in one wing for privacy

FIRST FLOOR — 2,679 SQ. FT.
BASEMENT — 2,679 SQ. FT.
GARAGE — 541 SQ. FT.

TOTAL LIVING AREA:
2,679 SQ. FT.

No. 9828

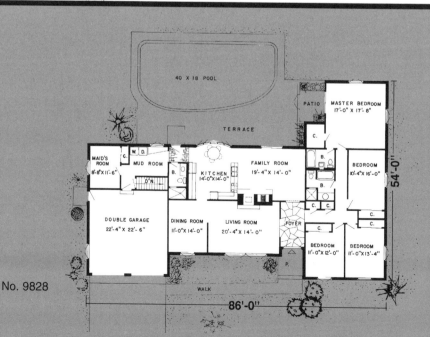

40 X 18 POOL

PATIO

MASTER BEDROOM
17'-0" X 17'-8"

TERRACE

BEDROOM
10'-4" X 16'-0"

MAID'S
ROOM
8'-8" X 11'-6"

MUD ROOM

KITCHEN
14'-0" X 14'-0"

FAMILY ROOM
19'-4" X 14'-0"

54'-0"

DOUBLE GARAGE
22'-4" X 22'-6"

DINING ROOM
11'-0" X 14'-0"

LIVING ROOM
20'-4" X 14'-0"

FOYER

BEDROOM
11'-0" X 12'-0"

BEDROOM
11'-0" X 13'-4"

WALK

86'-0"

No. 10507
Central Courtyard Features Pool

■ This plan features:
— Three bedrooms
— Two baths

■ A central courtyard complete with a pool

■ A secluded Master Bedroom accented by a sky light, spacious walk-in closet, and private bath

■ A convenient Kitchen easily serving the patio for comfortable outdoor entertaining

■ A detached two-car Garage

FIRST FLOOR — 2,194 SQ. FT.
GARAGE — 576 SQ. FT.

TOTAL LIVING AREA: 2,194 SQ. FT.

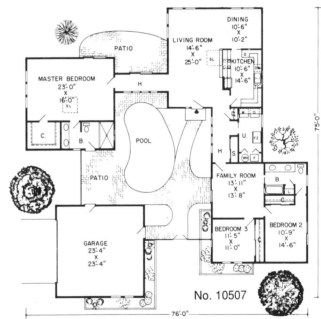

No. 10507

No. 34705
Colonial Home with All the Traditional Comforts

■ This plan features:
— Four bedrooms
— Two and one half baths

■ A formal Living Room and Dining Room flanking a spacious entry

■ Family areas flowing together into an open space at the rear of the home

■ An island Kitchen with a built-in pantry centrally located for easy service to the Dining Room and Breakfast area

■ A Master Suite including large closets and double vanities in the bath

FIRST FLOOR — 1,090 SQ. FT.
SECOND FLOOR — 1,134 SQ. FT.
BASEMENT — 1,090 SQ. FT.
GARAGE — 576 SQ. FT.

TOTAL LIVING AREA:
2,224 SQ. FT.

Second Floor

Br 4
11-4 x 10-8

MBr 1
13-8 x 15-6

Br 2
11-8 x 16

Br 3
11-4 x 10-8

Slab/Crawlspace Option

No. 34705

66'-0"

Kitchen
island 10-8 x 10-2
10-4 x 12-6

Brkfst

Family Rm
20 x 12-6

Garage
21-8 x 23-4

Dining Rm
13-8 x 12-6

Living
15 x 12-6

27'-0"

No. 270
Family Living for the Budget Minded

■ This plan features:
— Four bedrooms
— Three baths

■ A large efficient U-shaped Kitchen with double sink, ample cabinet and storage space and a peninsula counter dividing it from the Dining Room

■ A lovely Dining Room with access to a balcony and built-in china cabinet

■ A Master Suite with access to the balcony and a full private bath

■ Two additional first floor bedrooms, with ample closet space, that share a full hall bath

■ A lower floor equipped with Recreation Room, Hobby Room, Workshop and a bedroom with private bath

FIRST FLOOR — 1,456 SQ. FT.
LOWER FLOOR — 1,456 SQ. FT.
GARAGE — 528 SQ. FT.

TOTAL LIVING AREA:
2,912 SQ. FT.

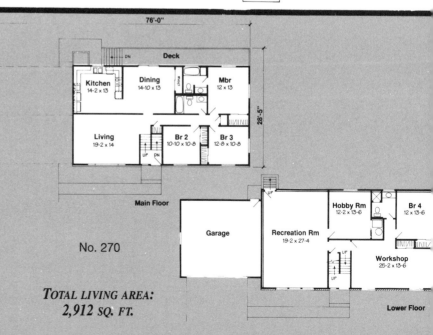

76'-0"

Deck

Kitchen
14-2 x 13

Dining
14-10 x 13

Mbr
12 x 13

Living
19-2 x 14

Br 2
10-10 x 10-8

Br 3
12-8 x 10-8

28'-5"

Main Floor

No. 270

Garage

Recreation Rm
19-2 x 27-4

Hobby Rm
12-2 x 13-6

Br 4
12 x 13-6

Workshop
25-2 x 13-6

Lower Floor

No. 10761
Tudor for Today & Tomorrow

■ This plan features:
— Four bedrooms
— Three and one half baths
■ Double doors opening to a huge entry foyer flanked by a formal Dining Room and a sunken Living Room
■ The cozy elegance of a book-lined Library
■ A Kitchen with a range top island and a sunny Breakfast room
■ A Master Suite with a fireplace, sitting area, and his-n-her closets

FIRST FLOOR — 1,926 SQ. FT.
SECOND FLOOR — 1,606 SQ. FT.
BASEMENT — 1,926 SQ. FT.
GARAGE — 840 SQ. FT.

TOTAL LIVING AREA:
3,532 SQ. FT.

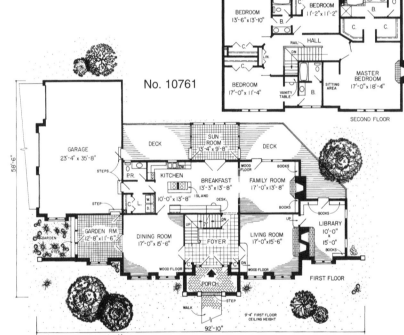

No. 24651
Cozy Homestead

- This plan features:
  — Three bedrooms
  — Two full baths
- Multi-paned windows and a country porch setting the theme for this comfortable home
- A spacious Living Room, enhanced by the natural light from the front window and the fireplace with built-in bookshelves flanking one side
- An efficient U-shaped Kitchen, located next to the Dining Room, with a walk-in pantry, double sink and a Breakfast Nook
- A convenient first floor Laundry Room to the left of the Breakfast Nook
- Private Master Suite with a whirlpool tub, separate shower, walk-in closet and tray ceiling
- Two additional bedrooms are located at the opposite side of the home from the Master Suite and share a full hall bath with a skylight

MAIN AREA — 1,821 SQ. FT.
GARAGE — 1,075 SQ. FT.
BASEMENT — 742 SQ. FT.

TOTAL LIVING AREA:
1,821 SQ. FT.

A Plan One Homes Inc. Design

No materials list available

No. 90629
A Home For All Seasons

- This plan features:
  — Three bedrooms
  — Three full and one half baths
- All rooms with outdoor decks
- A Living Room with a heat-circulating fireplace
- A Kitchen with ample counter and cabinet space and easy access to the Dining Room and outdoor dining area
- A Master Bedroom with a heat-circulating fireplace, plush Master Bath and a walk-in closet
- A basement foundation only

FIRST FLOOR — 1,001 SQ. FT.
SECOND FLOOR — 712 SQ. FT.
LOWER FLOOR — 463 SQ. FT.

TOTAL LIVING AREA:
2,176 SQ. FT.

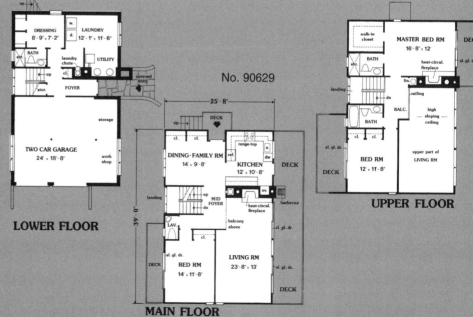

No. 34002
Affordable Ranch

■ This plan features:
— Three bedrooms
— One full bath

■ Sidelight front door opens into the bright Living Room with a triple window

■ An efficient U-shaped Kitchen adjacent to the Garage and the laundry easily serves the Dining area with open counter space

■ Access to the Patio from the Dining Room, expands the living space outdoors

■ Roomy Master Bedroom and two additional bedrooms with spacious closets

■ This plan is available with a Basement, Slab or Crawlspace foundation. Please specify when ordering

MAIN FLOOR — 1,092 SQ. FT.
GARAGE — 473 SQ. FT.

TOTAL LIVING AREA:
1,092 SQ. FT.

optional **Patio**   No. 34002

62'-0"

| Garage 19-8 x 23 | Kit 9 x 7 | Dining 8 x 7 | Br 3 9-8 x 10-3 | Br 2 11-6 x 10-3 |

DN | W D

Living Rm 20-11 x 11-7

MBr 1 11-6 x 10

26'-0"

Floor Plan

W D

Slab/crawlspace option

No. 10451
Secluded Bedroom

■ This plan features:
— Four bedrooms
— Three full and one half bath

■ A secluded Master Bedroom with a charming fireplace, individual dressing areas, and a sky-lit bathroom

■ A court yard effect created by the glassed-in living spaces overlooking the central covered patio

■ A sprawling charm which creates a sense of privacy everywhere you go

FIRST FLOOR — 2,864 SQ. FT.
GARAGE — 607 SQ. FT.

TOTAL LIVING AREA:
2,864 SQ. FT.

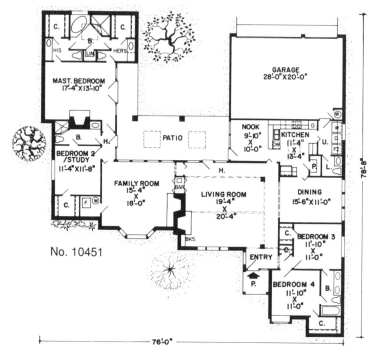

No. 10451

No. 10555
Stucco and Stone

■ This plan features:
— Three bedrooms
— Two and one half baths

■ A formal foyer leading through double doors into a well-designed library

■ A Master Bedroom offering vaulted ceilings and a huge bath area

■ An oversized Living Room with a fireplace

■ A utility room and half bath located next to the Garage

FIRST FLOOR — 1,671 SQ. FT.
SECOND FLOOR — 505 SQ. FT.
BASEMENT — 1,661 SQ. FT.
GARAGE — 604 SQ. FT.
SCREENED PORCH — 114 SQ. FT.

TOTAL LIVING AREA:
2,176 SQ. FT.

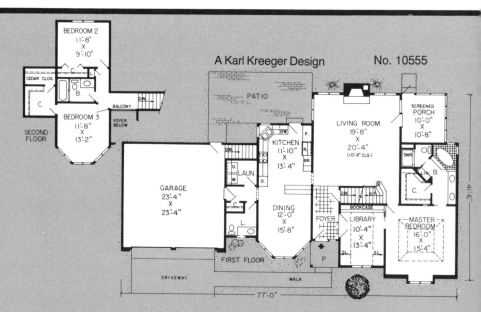

A Karl Kreeger Design   No. 10555

No. 20063
First-Time Owner's Delight

■ This plan features:
— Three bedrooms
— Two and one half baths

■ A distinctive exterior of wood veneer siding with a large, multi-paned picture window

■ A foyer leading directly into the Living Room which has a wood burning fireplace and opens to the Dining Room

■ A laundry room conveniently placed between the Kitchen and the Garage

■ A Master Bedroom on the first floor with a full bath and a walk-in closet

A loft area open to the Living Room below

First floor — 1,161 sq. ft.
Second floor — 631 sq. ft.

Total living area:
1,792 sq. ft.

An
EXCLUSIVE DESIGN
By Karl Kreeger

No. 20063

No. 34600
Rustic Exterior; Complete Home

- This plan features:
  — Three bedrooms
  — Two full baths
- A two-story, fireplaced Living Room with exposed beams add to rustic charm
- An efficient, modern Kitchen with ample work and storage space
- Two first floor bedrooms with individual closet space share full bath
- A Master Bedroom with privacy of second floor and its own full bath
- A welcoming front Porch adding to living space

FIRST FLOOR — 1,013 SQ. FT.
SECOND FLOOR — 315 SQ. FT.
BASEMENT — 1,008 SQ. FT.

TOTAL LIVING AREA: 1,328 SQ. FT.

36'-0"

No. 34600

Kitchen
17-4 x 10-8

Br 2
12 x 10-4

lin.

DN

Br 3
12 x 13

36'-0"

Living Rm
19-4 x 16-8
beamed ceiling

slope

UP

Deck

First Floor

MBr 1
12 x 13-8

DN

lin.

Second Floor

Slab/Crawlspace Option

No. 34003
Delightful, Compact Home

- This plan features:
  — Three bedrooms
  — Two full baths
- A fireplaced Living Room brightened by a wonderful picture window
- A counter island featuring double sinks separating the Kitchen and Dining areas
- A Master Bedroom including private Master Bath and double closets
- Two additional bedrooms with ample closet space and share full bath

FIRST FLOOR — 1,146 SQ. FT.

TOTAL LIVING AREA: 1,146 SQ. FT.

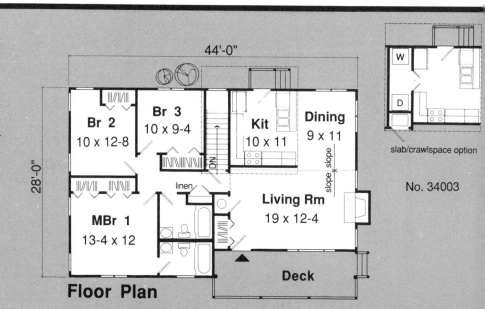

44'-0"

Br 2
10 x 12-8

Br 3
10 x 9-4

Kit
10 x 11

Dining
9 x 11

28'-0"

linen

MBr 1
13-4 x 12

Living Rm
19 x 12-4

Deck

Floor Plan

slab/crawlspace option

No. 34003

No. 20501
Home on a Hill

- This plan features:
  - Three bedrooms
  - Two full baths
- Window walls combining with sliders to unite active areas with a huge outdoor deck
- Interior spaces flowing together for an open feeling that is accentuated by the sloping ceilings and towering fireplace in the Living Room
- An island Kitchen with easy access to the Dining Room
- A Master Suite complete with a garden spa, abundant closet space, and a balcony

FIRST FLOOR — 1,316 SQ. FT.
SECOND FLOOR — 592 SQ. FT.

TOTAL LIVING AREA:
1,908 SQ. FT.

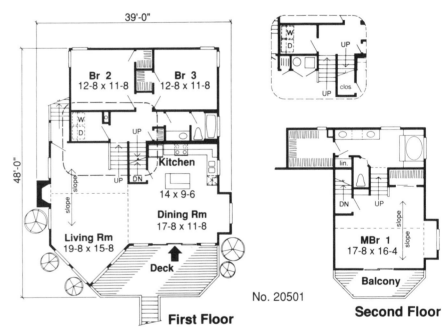

39'-0"

48'-0"

Br 2
12-8 x 11-8

Br 3
12-8 x 11-8

W
D

UP

UP

DN

Kitchen
14 x 9-6

Dining Rm
17-8 x 11-8

Living Rm
19-8 x 15-8

slope

Deck

First Floor

W
D

UP

UP

clos

lin.

DN

UP

slope
slope

MBr 1
17-8 x 16-4

Balcony

Second Floor

No. 20501

No. 34005
Decorative Detailing Adds Charm

■ This plan features:
— Three bedrooms
— One and one half baths
■ A Living Room with a cozy fireplace and sloped ceiling
■ An efficient Kitchen equipped with a plant shelf and within easy access to the Dining Room
■ A Master Bedroom with a decorative ceiling and a private bath
■ A second bath equipped with a washer and dryer

FIRST FLOOR — 1,441 SQ. FT.
GARAGE — 672 SQ. FT.

TOTAL LIVING AREA:
1,441 SQ. FT.

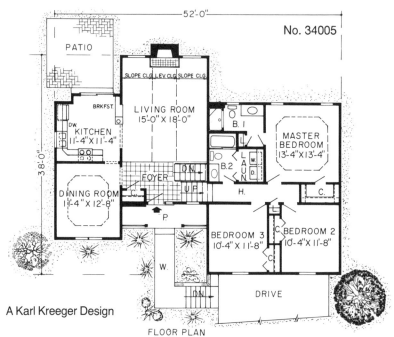

No. 34005

52'-0"

38'-0"

PATIO

SLOPE CLG. LEV CLG SLOPE CLG

LIVING ROOM
15'-0" X 18'-0"

BRKFST.

KITCHEN
11'-4" X 11'-4"

DW

B. I

MASTER
BEDROOM
13'-4" X 13'-4"

FOYER

DN
UP

B.2

LAUN
W.
D.

DINING ROOM
11'-4" X 12'-8"

H.

C.

BEDROOM 3
10'-4" X 11'-8"

C.

BEDROOM 2
10'-4" X 11'-8"

C.

P

W.

DN

DRIVE

FLOOR PLAN

A Karl Kreeger Design

No. 10493
Raised Ranch Offers Optional Basement Family Room

■ This plan features:
— Three bedrooms
— Two baths (optional future 1/2 bath)
■ A space saving lower level Garage offering the option of finishing the adjacent area at a future date
■ A Master Bedroom including walk-in closets
■ An activity area combining the Living and Dining Rooms into an open living space
■ A compact Kitchen packed with storage and a convenient laundry nook

FIRST FLOOR — 1,152 SQ. FT.
GARAGE — 572 SQ. FT.
BASEMENT — 550 SQ. FT.

TOTAL LIVING AREA:
1,152 SQ. FT.

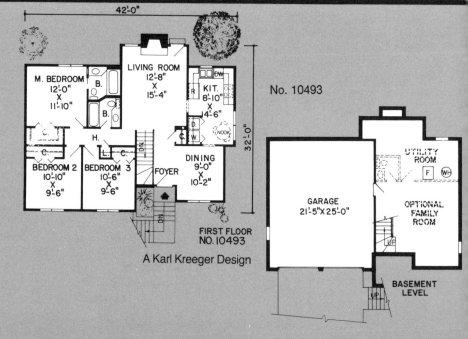

42'-0"

32'-0"

M. BEDROOM
12'-0"
X
11'-10"

B.

LIVING ROOM
12'-8"
X
15'-4"

KIT.
8'-10"
X
14'-6"

DW

No. 10493

B.

H.

C.

BEDROOM 2
10'-10"
X
9'-6"

BEDROOM 3
10'-6"
X
9'-6"

DN

FOYER

DINING
9'-0"
X
10'-2"

D
W
NOOK

DN

FIRST FLOOR
NO. 10493

A Karl Kreeger Design

UTILITY
ROOM

F

WH

GARAGE
21'-5" X 25'-0"

OPTIONAL
FAMILY
ROOM

UP

BASEMENT
LEVEL

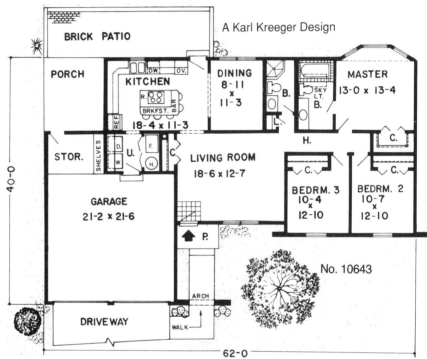

No. 10643

Low Maintenance, Southwestern Style

■ This plan features:

— Three bedrooms

— Two full baths

■ A cheerful Kitchen with a Breakfast bar and entry onto the patio

■ A sky-lit bath and huge bay window illuminating the Master Suite

■ A spacious Living Room, convenient Dining Room, and a handy utility room

FIRST FLOOR — 1,285 SQ. FT.

GARAGE — 473 SQ. FT.

TOTAL LIVING AREA: 1,285 SQ. FT.

A Karl Kreeger Design

BRICK PATIO

PORCH

KITCHEN
DW. OV.
R.
BRKFST. BAR
REF.
18-4 x 11-3

DINING
8-11 x 11-3

B.
SKY LT.
B.

MASTER
13-0 x 13-4

STOR.
SHELVES
D. F.
U. C.
W. H.

LIVING ROOM
18-6 x 12-7

H.

C.

GARAGE
21-2 x 21-6

P.

BEDRM. 3
10-4 x 12-10

BEDRM. 2
10-7 x 12-10

DRIVEWAY

ARCH

WALK

No. 10643

40-0

62-0

No. 91002
Lovely Second Home

■ This plan features:
— Three bedrooms
— Two full baths
■ Firedrum fireplace warming both entryway and Living Room
■ Dining and Living Rooms opening onto the deck, which surrounds the house on three sides
■ A crawl space foundation

FIRST FLOOR — 808 SQ. FT.
SECOND FLOOR — 288 SQ. FT.

**TOTAL LIVING AREA:
1,096 SQ. FT.**

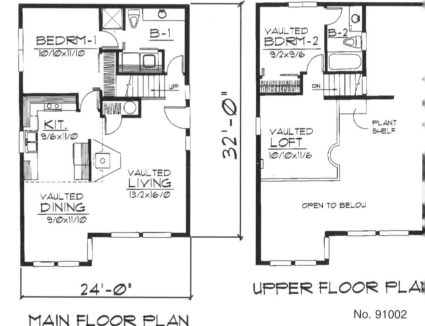

MAIN FLOOR PLAN

UPPER FLOOR PLAN

No. 91002

No. 24701
Convenient Floor Plan

■ This plan features:
— Three bedrooms
— Two full baths
■ Central Foyer leads to Den/Guest room with arched window below vaulted ceiling and Living Room accented by two-sided fireplace
■ Efficient, U-shaped Kitchen with peninsula counter/breakfast bar serving Dining Room and adjacent Utility/Pantry
■ Master Suite features large walk-in closet and private bath with double vanity and whirlpool tub
■ Two additional bedrooms with ample closet space share full bath

MAIN FLOOR — 1,625 SQ. FT.
BASEMENT — 1,625 SQ. FT.
FOUNDATION — BASEMENT, SLAB OR CRAWL SPACE

**TOTAL LIVING AREA :
1,625 SQ. FT.**

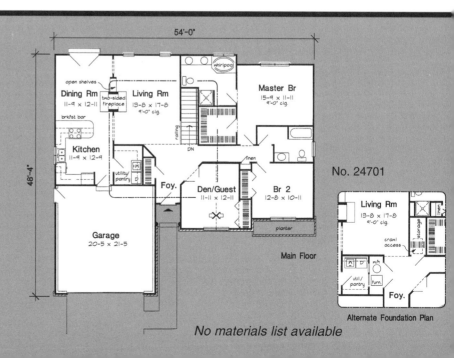

No. 24701

No materials list available

No. 90125
Open Floor Plan Enhanced by Sloped Ceilings

■ This plan features:
  — Three bedrooms
  — Two full baths
■ A step down into the tiled entrance area
■ An open Great Room and Living Room enhanced by sloping ceilings, cozy fireplace, and sliding doors to back patio
■ An L shaped Kitchen sharing snack bar with Dining Room
■ An optional basement or crawlspace foundation — please specify when ordering

MAIN AREA — 1,440 SQ. FT.

TOTAL LIVING AREA: 1,440 SQ. FT.

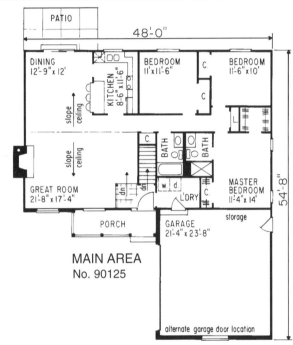

MAIN AREA
No. 90125

No. 93206
Distinctive Brick with Room to Expand

■ This plan features:
— Four bedrooms
— Two and half baths

■ Arched entrance with decorative glass leads into two-story Foyer

■ Formal Dining Room with tray ceiling above decorative window

■ Efficient Kitchen with island cooktop and built-in desk and pantry easily serves Breakfast area and adjacent Dining Room

■ Master Bedroom wing topped by tray ceiling with French door to Patio, huge private bath with garden tub, two walk-in closets and vanities

■ Three additional bedrooms with ample closets share laundry and full bath

■ Second Floor optional space for Storage and huge Future Bedroom with full bath

FIRST FLOOR — 2,645 SQ. FT.
FUTURE SECOND FLOOR — 619 SQ. FT.
BASEMENT — 2,561 SQ. FT.
GARAGE — 560 SQ. FT.
FOUNDATION — BASEMENT ONLY

A Jannis Vann & Associates, Inc. Des

FIRST FLOOR
No. 93206

TOTAL LIVING AREA:
2,645 SQ. FT.

SECOND FLOOR

No. 90696
Energy-Saving Cape

■ This plan features:
— Four bedrooms
— Two full baths

■ A large Living Room with an exposed wood beam ceiling, heat-circulating fireplace and a bay window

■ A sunny Dining and Family Room enlarged by a bay window with sliding glass doors to a rear deck

■ A country Kitchen with generous cabinet and counter space

■ A first floor Master Bedroom with his-n-her closets

■ Two additional upstairs bedrooms with sitting areas and skylights

FIRST FLOOR — 1,382 SQ. FT.
SECOND FLOOR — 688 SQ. FT.

TOTAL LIVING AREA:
2,070 SQ. FT.

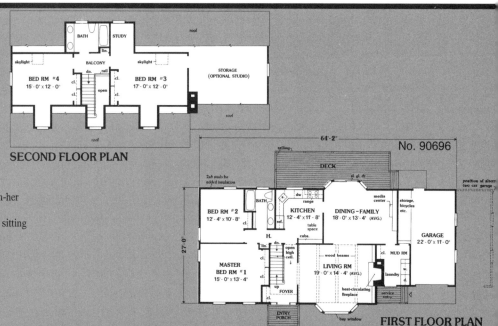

SECOND FLOOR PLAN

No. 90696

FIRST FLOOR PLAN

No. 91613
Stucco Splendor

■ This plan features:
— Three bedrooms
— Three full baths

■ A cozy Den with an adjoining full bath and French doors

■ A coved ceiling in both the Living and Dining Rooms

■ An efficient, cook-top island Kitchen with more than ample counter and storage space

■ A glass-walled eating Nook

■ A built-in wetbar and a fireplace in the Family Room

■ An enchanting Master Suite with a private sitting room, fabulous spa bath and a walk-in closet

FIRST FLOOR — 2,268 SQ. FT.
SECOND FLOOR — 1,484 SQ. FT.
BONUS ROOM — 300 SQ. FT.

TOTAL LIVING AREA: 3,752 SQ. FT.

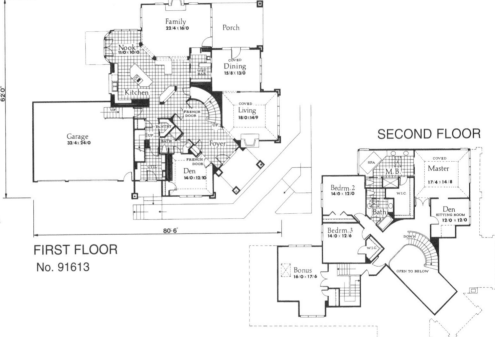

FIRST FLOOR
No. 91613

SECOND FLOOR

No. 24654
Country Influence

- This plan features:
  — Three bedrooms
  — Two full baths
- Front Porch entry into unique Sun Room with half bath and coat closet
- Open Living Room enhanced by palladium window, focal point fireplace and atrium door to Deck
- Bay window brightens formal Dining Room conveniently located between Living Room and Kitchen
- Efficient L-shaped Kitchen with bay window eating area, laundry closet and handy Garage entrance
- Plush Master Bedroom offers another bay window crowned by tray ceiling and private bath with double vanity
- Two additional bedrooms with arched window and ample closets share full bath

No materials list available

A Plan One Homes Inc. Design

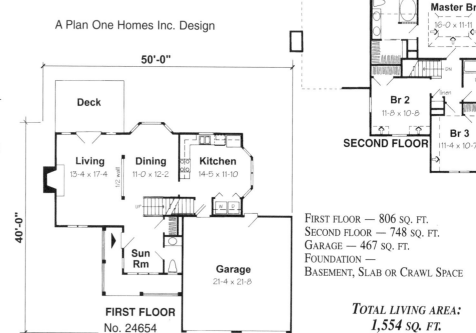

Master Br
16-0 x 11-11

Br 2
11-8 x 10-8

SECOND FLOOR

Br 3
11-4 x 10-7

50'-0"

Deck

Living
13-4 x 17-4

Dining
11-0 x 12-2

Kitchen
14-5 x 11-10

1/2 wall

UP

40'-0"

Sun Rm

Garage
21-4 x 21-8

FIRST FLOOR
No. 24654

FIRST FLOOR — 806 SQ. FT.
SECOND FLOOR — 748 SQ. FT.
GARAGE — 467 SQ. FT.
FOUNDATION —
BASEMENT, SLAB OR CRAWL SPACE

TOTAL LIVING AREA:
1,554 SQ. FT.

No. 90105
Great Room Features Fireplace

- This plan features:
  — Three bedrooms
  — Two full baths
- A spacious Great Room with a cozy fireplace
- A Kitchen with a pass through serving for convenience
- A combination Mud Room/Laundry room, to make cleaning up a breeze
- An optional basement, slab or crawl space foundation — please specify when ordering

MAIN AREA — 1,345 SQ. FT.

TOTAL LIVING AREA:
1,345 SQ. FT.

No. 90105

PATIO
66'-0"

BEDROOM
11-5"x10-4"

BEDROOM
10-10"x9-4"

DINING ROOM
12'x9'

KITCHEN
11'x8-8"

MUD ROOM

STORAGE

30'-5"

pass thru

GARAGE
21-4"x20-3"

BATH

GREAT ROOM
20-7"x16'

MASTER BEDROOM
11-5"x13-9"

BATH

PORCH

alternate door location

No. 10787
Compact Comfort

■ This plan features:
— Three bedrooms
— Two and one half baths
■ Soaring ceilings and a wall of stacked windows
■ A formal Dining Room perfect for entertaining
■ A Kitchen/Family Room combination with a cozy fireplace
■ An efficient Kitchen layout
■ Three bedrooms upstairs and two full baths, including the luxury bath in the Master Bedroom

FIRST FLOOR — 1,088 SQ. FT.
SECOND FLOOR — 750 SQ. FT.
BASEMENT — 750 SQ. FT.
GARAGE — 548 SQ. FT.

TOTAL LIVING AREA:
1,838 SQ. FT.

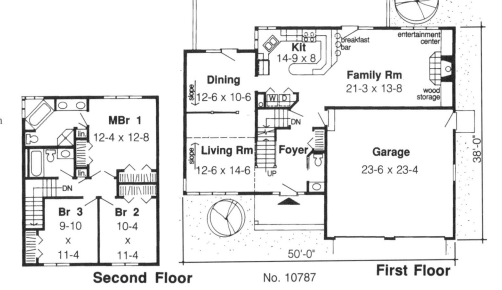

Second Floor

MBr 1
12-4 x 12-8

Br 3
9-10
x
11-4

Br 2
10-4
x
11-4

DN

lin.
lin.

Patio

Kit
14-9 x 8

breakfast bar

entertainment center

Dining
12-6 x 10-6

Family Rm
21-3 x 13-8

wood storage

W D

DN

slope

Living Rm
12-6 x 14-6

Foyer

UP

Garage
23-6 x 23-4

38'-0"

50'-0"

First Floor

No. 10787

No. 91055
Excellent Choice for First Time Buyer

■ This plan features:
— Three bedrooms
— Two and a half baths

■ A friendly, covered Porch sheltering the front entrance

■ A formal Living Room with an expansive floor-to-ceiling triple window flowing into a formal Dining Room

■ A comfortable Family Room with a sliding glass door to the backyard, a Utility Closet with washer and dryer and access to the Kitchen

■ An efficient Kitchen with a peninsula counter/snackbar on the Family Room side and adjacent to the Dining Room for ease in serving

■ A cozy Master Bedroom with a recessed dormer window, an oversized, walk-in closet and a private Bath

■ Two additional bedrooms, on the second floor, sharing a full hall bath and a Playroom that could be a fourth bedroom

FIRST FLOOR — 805 SQ. FT.
SECOND FLOOR — 961 SQ. FT.
GARAGE — 540 SQ. FT.

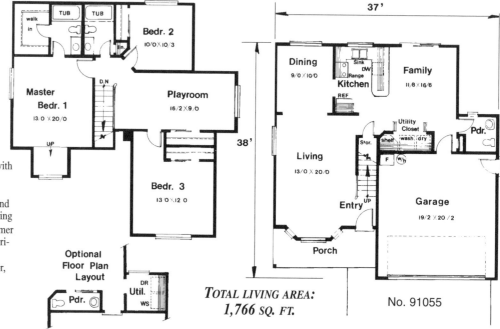

TOTAL LIVING AREA:
1,766 SQ. FT.

No. 91055

No. 91728
Angled Elegance

■ This plan features:
— Three bedrooms
— Two full and one half baths

■ An angled design for exterior and interior drama

■ A handy and inconspicuous Pantry in the hallway for added convenience

■ A step-down Living Room secluded from the rest of the floor plan

FIRST FLOOR — 1,285 SQ. FT.
BASEMENT FLOOR — 629 SQ. FT.
WIDTH — 78'-0"
DEPTH — 51'-0"

TOTAL LIVING AREA:
1,914 SQ. FT.
PROOFED

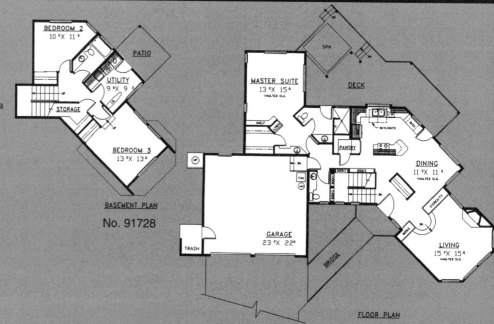

No. 91728

No. 90826
Watch the World Go By

■ This plan features:
— Three or four bedrooms
— Three full and one half baths
■ A large wrap-around porch
■ An immense Living Room, highlighted by a fieldstone fireplace
■ A Study or Guest Room with easy access to a full bath
■ A central work island Kitchen
■ Open floor plan between the Kitchen and the Family Room
■ A formal Dining Room with direct access to the Kitchen and views of the front porch
■ A Sewing room and a Utility Room separated by a powder room
■ A large Master Suite served by a private bath and huge walk-in closet

FIRST FLOOR — 1,463 SQ. FT.
SECOND FLOOR — 981 SQ. FT.
BASEMENT — 814 SQ. FT.

TOTAL LIVING AREA:
2,444 SQ. FT.

FIRST FLOOR
No. 90826

WIDTH — 59'-0"
DEPTH — 34'-0"

A Westhome Planners, Ltd. Design

SECOND FLOOR

No. 26114
High Windows Add Light

■ This plan features:

— Three bedrooms

— One full and one half baths

■ A covered Entry steps down into the spacious Living/Dining Room featuring a vaulted ceiling, a fireplace and sliding glass doors to expansive Deck area

■ An efficient, U-shaped Kitchen with a peninsula counter adjoining the Dining Room

■ A first floor Bedroom/Den with a triple window and a walk-in closet

■ Two additional bedrooms on the second floor share a balcony and a full bath

FIRST FLOOR — 696 SQ. FT.
SECOND FLOOR — 416 SQ. FT.
BASEMENT — 696 SQ. FT.

TOTAL LIVING AREA:
1,112 SQ. FT.

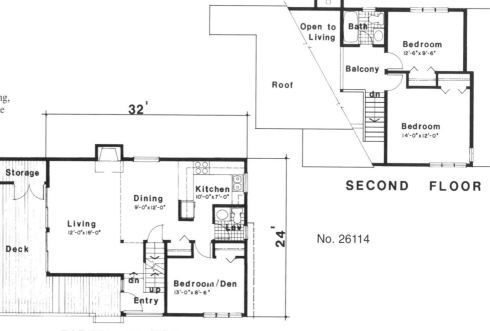

SECOND FLOOR

No. 26114

FIRST FLOOR

No. 10595
Perfect for a Hillside

■ This plan features:

— Three bedrooms

— Two and one half baths

■ An island Kitchen with a breakfast area leading onto one of two screened porches

■ A huge Recreation Room with a Kitchenette and fireplace

■ A sloping ceiling and fireplace in the spacious Living Room

■ A central staircase directing traffic to all areas of the house

FIRST FLOOR — 1,643 SQ. FT.
SECOND FLOOR — 1,297 SQ. FT.
GARAGE — 528 SQ. FT.

TOTAL LIVING AREA:
2,940 SQ. FT.

A Karl Kreeger Design

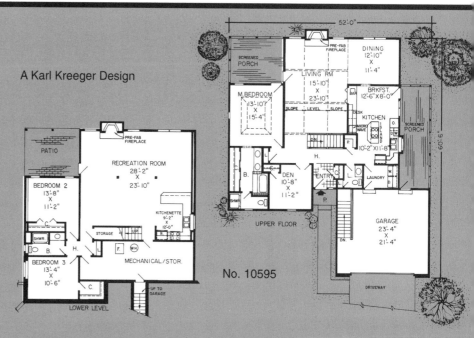

No. 10595

No. 34013
Bay Windows and Fieldstone Accents

This plan features:

— Three bedrooms
— Two full baths

■ Recessed entrance framed by gracious bay windows leads into unique octagon foyer

■ Formal Dining Room features highlighted by bay window below decorative ceiling

■ Sloped ceiling crowns Living Room with tiled, hearth fireplace and sliding glass door to Deck

■ Efficient Kitchen with angled snackbar counter easily accesses Breakfast area, Dining Room, Laundry area and Garage entry

■ Bright Breakfast area with access to covered Deck, built-in desk and expansive outdoor views

■ Corner Master Bedroom suite with decorative ceiling, boxed window and dressing area with a double vanity and walk-in closet

■ Two additional bedrooms with decorative windows and walk-in closets, share a full bath

MAIN AREA
No. 34013

76'-0"

60'-6"

DECK

COVERED DECK

BRKFST.
9'-6"
X
8'-0"

LIVING RM.
13'-0"
X
17'-4"

SLOPE   SLOPE

MAST. BEDROOM
15'-8"
X
11'-4"

B.

KITCHEN
12'-0" X 10'-6"

DW

DINING
11'-0"
X
13'-6"

FOYER

BEDROOM 3
11'-0"
X
13'-6"

H.

DRESSING

B.

C.

BEDROOM 2
11'-4"
X
11'-6"

C.

C.

W   D

L.   D

GARAGE
21'-8"
X
22'-0"

MAIN FLOOR — 1,803 SQ. FT.
GARAGE — 480 SQ. FT.
FOUNDATION — BASEMENT, SLAB OR CRAWL SPACE

TOTAL LIVING AREA:
1,803 SQ. FT.

No. 20051
Three Bedroom Features Cathedral Ceilings

■ This plan features:
— Three bedrooms
— Two and a half baths
■ A Kitchen with central island, built-in desk, pantry and adjacent Breakfast Nook
■ A fireplaced Living Room with built-in book case that combines with the Dining Room
■ A Master Suite with private full bath

FIRST FLOOR — 1,285 SQ. FT.
SECOND FLOOR — 490 SQ. FT.
BASEMENT — 1,285 SQ. FT.
GARAGE — 495 SQ. FT.

TOTAL LIVING AREA:
1,775 SQ. FT.

A Karl Kreeger Design

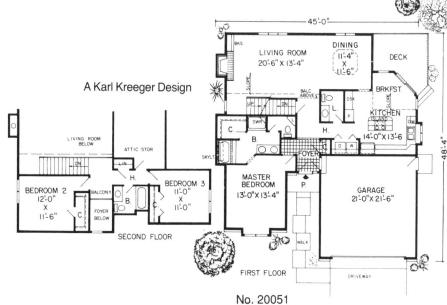

No. 20051

No. 10524
Split-level Made for Growing Family

■ This plan features:
— Four bedrooms
— Two and three quarters baths
■ A fireplaced Living Room, stepping up to a Dining Room with adjoining Kitchen
■ An efficient Kitchen featuring an eat-in space and sliding door access to the deck

FIRST FLOOR — 1,470 SQ. FT.
SECOND FLOOR — 711 SQ. FT.
BASEMENT — 392 SQ. FT.
GARAGE — 563 SQ. FT.

TOTAL LIVING AREA:
2,181 SQ. FT.

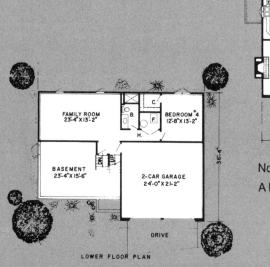

No. 10524
A Karl Kreeger Design

No. 20310
Custom Windows Light Up Contemporary

■ This plan features:
— Three bedrooms
— Two and a half baths

■ A Master Bedroom with a volume ceiling, walk-in closet and private Master Bath

■ A fireplaced Great Room flowing into an elegant Dining Room with floor to ceiling windows

■ An island Kitchen with an eating Nook and easy access to Dining Room

FIRST FLOOR — 1,263 SQ. FT.
SECOND FLOOR — 483 SQ. FT.
GARAGE — 528 SQ. FT.
BASEMENT — 1,263 SQ. FT.

TOTAL LIVING AREA:
1,746 SQ. FT.

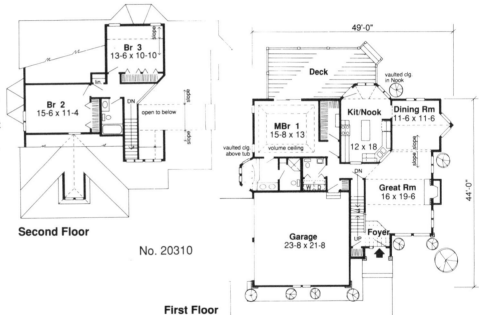

Second Floor

No. 20310

- Br 3
  13-6 x 10-10
- Br 2
  15-6 x 11-4
- open to below

49'-0"

Deck

vaulted clg. in Nook

MBr 1
15-8 x 13
vaulted clg. above tub
volume ceiling

Kit/Nook
12 x 18

Dining Rm
11-6 x 11-6

Great Rm
16 x 19-6

Garage
23-8 x 21-8

Foyer

44'-0"

First Floor

No. 20179
Classic Style

■ This plan features:
— Four bedrooms
— Two full and one half baths

■ An efficient island Kitchen with ample storage and counter space, a laundry center and a sunny Breakfast nook

■ A sunken Hearth Room with sloped ceiling and cozy fireplace

■ A formal Living Room and Dining Room that flow conveniently into each other for easy entertaining

■ A Master Suite with a decorative ceiling, private Master Bath and ample closet space

■ Three additional bedrooms that share a full hall bath

FIRST FLOOR — 1,086 SQ. FT.
SECOND FLOOR — 1,057 SQ. FT.
BASEMENT — 881 SQ. FT.
GARAGE — 484 SQ. FT.

TOTAL LIVING AREA:
2,143 SQ. FT.

A Karl Kreeger Design

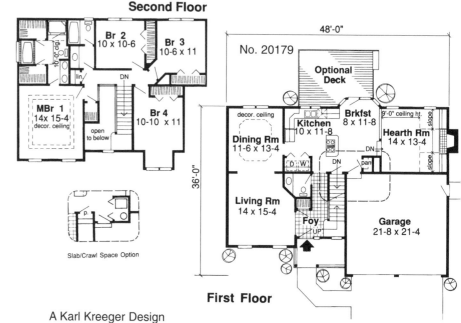

Second Floor

Br 2 10 x 10-6
Br 3 10-6 x 11
MBr 1 14 x 15-4 decor. ceiling
Br 4 10-10 x 11
open to below

Slab/Crawl Space Option

First Floor

No. 20179
48'-0"
36'-0"

Optional Deck

Dining Rm 11-6 x 13-4
Kitchen 10 x 11-8
Brkfst 8 x 11-8
9'-0" ceiling ht.
Hearth Rm 14 x 13-4
decor. ceiling
Living Rm 14 x 15-4
Foy
Garage 21-8 x 21-4

No. 10579
Attractive Rock Fireplace in Split Level

■ This plan features:
— Three bedrooms
— Two full baths

■ A covered Porch leads into a tiled Foyer and easy access to the lower level Garage

■ An expansive formal Dining/Great Room accented by an open beamed, sloping ceiling, a bay window and a bold rock fireplace

■ An L-shaped eat-in Kitchen opens to the Patio and the Dining area

■ A spacious Master Suite offering a walk-in closet and a full bath

■ Two bedrooms with oversized closets share a full hall bath

■ A Loft area

FIRST FLOOR — 1,400 SQ. FT.
LOFT — 142 SQ. FT.
BASEMENT — 663 SQ. FT.
GARAGE — 680 SQ. FT.

TOTAL LIVING AREA:
1,542 SQ. FT.

A Karl Kreeger Design

GARAGE 23'-0" X 27'-4"
APRON DRIVEWAY
LOWER FLOOR PLAN

LOFT 12'-4" X 7'-0"
LOFT PLAN
CLERESTORY WINDOWS

No. 20179

PATIO
BEDROOM 2 10'-0" X 11'-6"
BEDROOM 3 10'-6" X 9'-10"
KITCHEN 12'-4" X 13'-4"
FORMAL DINING AREA
SKYLIGHT
M. BEDROOM 14'-0" X 11'-10"
GREAT ROOM 13'-10" X 22'-0"
FOYER
30'-0"
51'-0"
DRIVEWAY BELOW
WALK
Main Area

No. 10501
Foyer Welcomes Guests

■ This plan features:
— Four bedrooms
— Two full and two half baths

■ A massive welcoming foyer which steps right into the Great Room

■ A Great Room enlarged by a wrap-around deck and highlighted by a fireplace, built-in bookcases, and a wetbar

■ A Kitchen with a built-in desk, an octagonal morning room, and a central island

FIRST FLOOR — 2,419 SQ. FT.
SECOND FLOOR — 926 SQ. FT.
BASEMENT — 2,419 SQ. FT.
GARAGE — 615 SQ. FT.

TOTAL LIVING AREA:
3,345 SQ. FT.

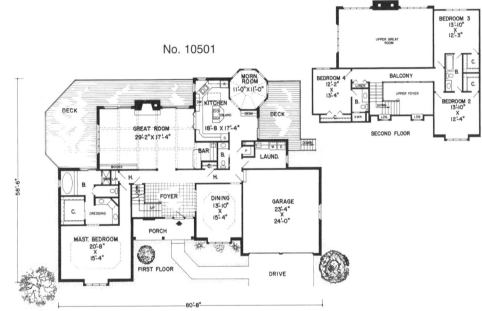

No. 10501

A Karl Kreeger Design

No. 34037
Arched Windows Add Light and Style

■ This plan features:
— Three bedrooms
— Two full and one half baths

■ A sheltered entry into Foyer flanked by formal Living and Dining rooms

■ An expansive Family Room with a focal point fireplace between decorative windows

■ An open Kitchen/Breakfast area offers a work island/snackbar, built-in pantry, sliding glass door to Deck, and Utility/Garage entrance

■ A first floor Master Bedroom enhanced by a double vanity bath and a large walk-in closet

FIRST FLOOR — 1,880 SQ. FT.
SECOND FLOOR — 575 SQ. FT.
GARAGE — 564 SQ. FT.
FOUNDATION — BASEMENT, SLAB OR CRAWL SPACE

TOTAL LIVING AREA: 2,455 SQ. FT.

No. 34037

Second Floor
Br 3 11-0 x13-4 — skylight
lin.
Br 2 12-0 x13-4 — open to foyer
dn.

First Floor
optional Fireplace
optional Deck
Family Rm 16-0 x23-4 (10' ceil.)
M. Bedroom 16-0 x13-4
Kit/Brkfst 18-8x 13-4
U.
dw
desk
pan.
lin.
dn.
Dining Rm 12-0 x13-0
Living Rm 13-0 x 15-4
up
Foyer
Garage 22-4 x25-4
52'0"
67'0"

Slab/Crawlspace Option

No. 90930
A-Frame for Year-Round Living

■ This plan features:
— Three bedrooms
— Two full baths

■ A vaulted ceiling in the Living Room with a massive fireplace

■ A wrap-around sun deck that gives you a lot of outdoor living space

■ A luxurious Master Suite complete with a walk-in closet, full bath and private deck

■ Two additional bedrooms that share a full hall bath

FIRST FLOOR — 1,238 SQ. FT.
LOFT — 464 SQ. FT.
BASEMENT — 1,175 SQ. FT.
WIDTH — 34'-0"
DEPTH — 56'-0"

TOTAL LIVING AREA: 1,702 SQ. FT.

A Westhome Planners, Ltd. Design

No. 90930

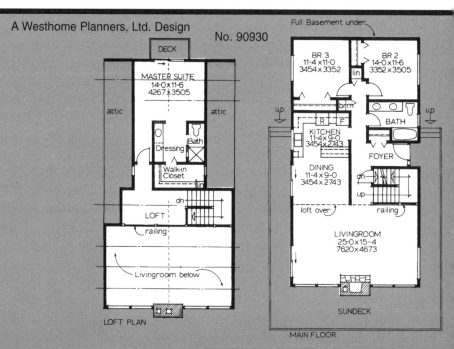

DECK
MASTER SUITE 14-0 x11-6 4267 x3505
attic
attic
Dressing
Bath
Walk-in Closet
dn
LOFT
railing
Livingroom below
LOFT PLAN

Full Basement under
BR 3 11-4 x11-0 3454 x 3352
BR 2 14-0 x11-6 3352 x 3505
lin
up
BATH
up
KITCHEN 11-4x 9-0 3454 x2743
FOYER
R F
DINING 11-4 x 9-0 3454 x 2743
dn
up
loft over
railing
LIVINGROOM 25-0 x15-4 7620 x4673
SUNDECK
MAIN FLOOR

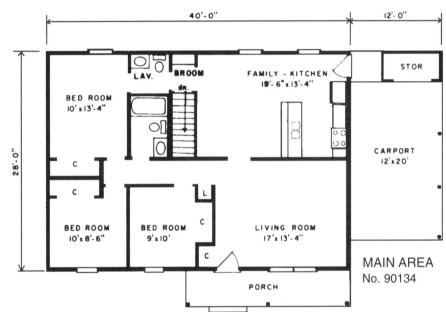

No. 90134

Extra Large Family Kitchen in Cozy Three Bedroom

■ This plan features:
— Three bedrooms
— One full and one half baths

■ A sheltered porch providing a protected entrance

■ An extra large Kitchen, with a galley-style food preparation area, separated from the rest of the room by an eating bar

■ Three bedrooms clustered around the full bath

■ A large outdoor storage area built into the back of the carport

■ An optional basement, slab or crawl space foundation — please specify when ordering

MAIN AREA — 1,120 SQ. FT.

TOTAL LIVING AREA:
1,120 SQ. FT.

MAIN AREA
No. 90134

No. 10549
Brick Design has Striking Exterior

■ This plan features:
— Three bedrooms
— Three full and one half baths

■ A circle-head window that sets off a striking exterior

■ A Master Bedroom including a sloping ceiling, large closet space, and a private bath with both a tub and shower

■ A Great Room with impressive open crossed beams and a wood-burning fireplace

■ A Kitchen with access to the Dining Room and Breakfast Room

FIRST FLOOR — 2,280 SQ. FT.
BASEMENT — 2,280 SQ. FT.
GARAGE — 528 SQ. FT.

TOTAL LIVING AREA:
2,280 SQ. FT.

No. 10549
A Karl Kreeger Design

No. 20191
Exciting Ceilings

■ This plan features:
— Three bedrooms
— Two full baths

■ A brick hearth fireplace in the Living Room

■ An efficient Kitchen with an island and double sinks that flows into the Dining Room with decorative ceiling

■ A private Master Suite with a decorative ceiling and Master Bath

■ Two additional bedrooms that share a full bath

FIRST FLOOR — 1,606 SQ. FT.
BASEMENT — 1,575 SQ. FT.
GARAGE — 545 SQ. FT.

TOTAL LIVING AREA:
1,606 SQ. FT.

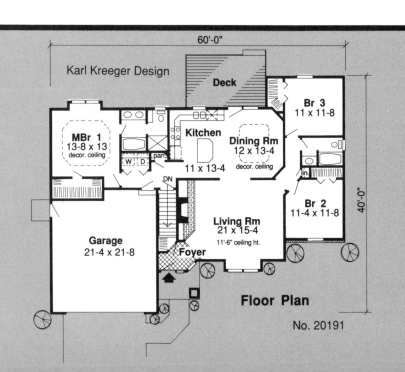

Karl Kreeger Design

Floor Plan

No. 20191

No. 10737

Modern Tudor is Hard to Resist

A Karl Kreeger Design

■ This plan features:
— Four bedrooms
— Three and one half baths

■ A seven-sided Breakfast room, an island Kitchen adjoining the Formal Dining Room

■ A beamed Family Room with private Study

■ A Master Suite complete with sauna, whirlpool, double vanity and fireplace

First floor — 2,457 sq. ft.
Second floor — 1,047 sq. ft.
Basement — 2,457 sq. ft.
Garage — 837 sq. ft.
Sun room — 213 sq. ft.

TOTAL LIVING AREA:
3,504 SQ. FT.

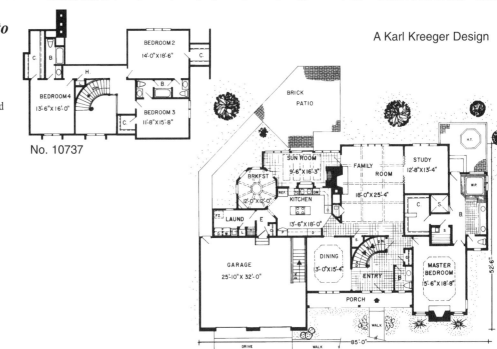

No. 10737

No. 90986
Surrounded with Sunshine

A Westhome Planners, Ltd. Design

WIDTH: 74' - 0"
DEPTH: 45' - 0"

■ This plan features:
— Three bedrooms
— Two full and one half baths

■ An Italianate style, featuring columns and tile originally designed to sit on the edge of a golf course

■ An open design with pananoramic vistas in every direction

■ Tile used from the Foyer, into the Kitchen and Nook, as well as in the Utility Room

■ A whirlpool tub in the elaborate and spacious Master Bedroom suite

■ A Great Room with a corner gas fireplace

■ A turreted Breakfast Nook and an efficient Kitchen with peninsula counter

■ Two family bedrooms that share a full hall bath

MAIN AREA — 1,731 SQ. FT.
GARAGE — 888 SQ. FT.

TOTAL LIVING AREA:
1,731 SQ. FT.

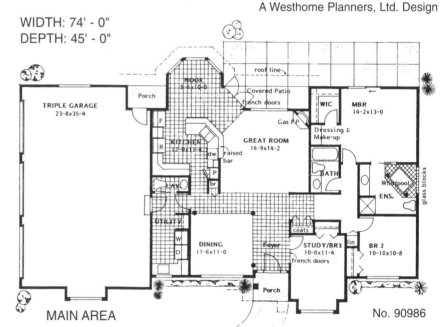

MAIN AREA

No. 90986

No. 91026
Home on a Hill

■ This plan features:
— Two bedrooms
— Two full baths

■ Sweeping panels of glass and a wood stove, creating atmosphere for the Great Room

■ An open plan that draws the Kitchen into the warmth of the Great Room's wood stove

■ A sleeping loft that has a full bath all to itself

■ A basement foundation only

FIRST FLOOR — 988 SQ. FT.
SECOND FLOOR — 366 SQ. FT.
BASEMENT — 988 SQ. FT.

TOTAL LIVING AREA:
1,354 SQ. FT.

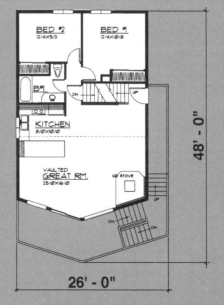

MAIN FLOOR PLAN

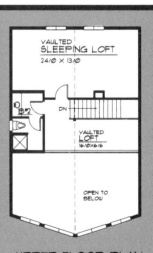

UPPER FLOOR PLAN
No. 91026

No. 90838
Room to Grow

■ This plan features:

— Three bedrooms

— Three full baths

■ A corner gas fireplace in the spacious Living Room

■ A Master Suite including a private Bath with a whirlpool tub, separate shower and a double vanity

■ An island Kitchen that is well-equipped to efficiently serve both formal Dining Room and informal Nook

■ Two additional bedrooms sharing a full bath on the second floor

FIRST FLOOR — 1,837 SQ. FT.

SECOND FLOOR — 848 SQ. FT.

BASEMENT — 1,803 SQ. FT.

BONUS ROOM — 288 SQ. FT.

**TOTAL LIVING AREA:
2,685 SQ. FT.
PROOFED**

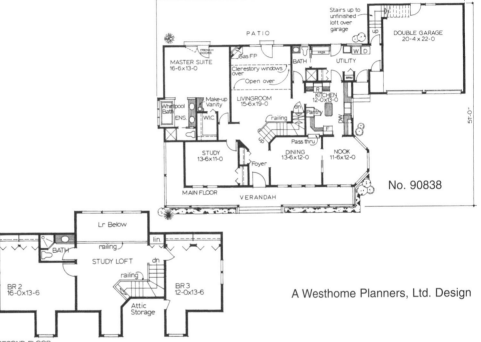

A Westhome Planners, Ltd. Design

No. 24305
Contemporary Living

■ This plan features:
— Three bedrooms
— Two full baths

■ A split-level with an open living area, so that the Kitchen, Living Room and Dining Room flow into each other

■ A U-shaped Kitchen with double sink and plenty of storage and counter area

■ A spacious Living Room, with a large multi-paned window offering natural light, and a view of the front yard

■ A Dining Room convenient to the Kitchen, with direct access to the patio

■ A Master Suite with a private bath that includes a step-in shower

■ Two additional bedrooms that share a full hall bath

MAIN AREA — 984 SQ. FT.
BASEMENT — 442 SQ. FT.
GARAGE — 393 SQ. FT.

TOTAL LIVING AREA:
984 SQ. FT.

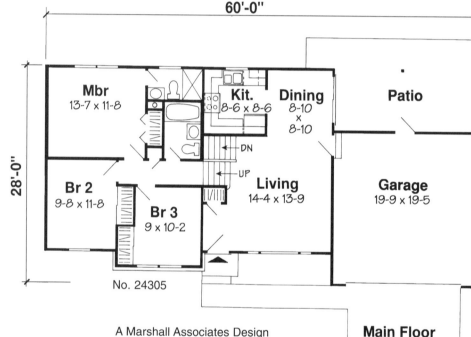

60'-0"

28'-0"

| Mbr 13-7 x 11-8 | | Kit. 8-6 x 8-6 | Dining 8-10 x 8-10 | Patio |

DN
UP

Br 2 9-8 x 11-8
Br 3 9 x 10-2
Living 14-4 x 13-9
Garage 19-9 x 19-5

No. 24305

A Marshall Associates Design

Main Floor

No. 1064
Functional Family Room

■ This plan features:
— Four bedrooms
— Two full baths

■ Sheltered front porch leading into a tiled Foyer area and a formal Living Room with a bay window

■ Family Room featuring a heat-circulating fireplace flanked by bookshelves, a television shelf and a wood storage area

■ An efficient U-shaped Kitchen with a snack bar adjacent to the Utility Room/Garage and the Family Room

■ A Master Bedroom which offers two closets and a private bath

■ Three additional bedrooms share a full hall bath

MAIN FLOOR — 1,954 SQ . FT.
GARAGE — 431 SQ. FT.

TOTAL LIVING AREA:
1,954 SQ. FT.

MAIN AREA
No. 1064

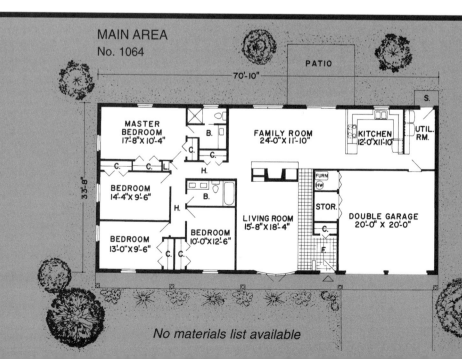

PATIO

70'-10"

33'-8"

| MASTER BEDROOM 17'-8" X 10'-4" | | FAMILY ROOM 24'-0" X 11'-10" | KITCHEN 12'-0" X 11'-10" | UTIL. RM. |

BEDROOM 14'-4" X 9'-6"

FURN
HW
STOR.

BEDROOM 13'-0" X 9'-6"
BEDROOM 10'-0" X 12'-6"
LIVING ROOM 15'-8" X 18'-4"
DOUBLE GARAGE 20'-0" X 20'-0"

No materials list available

166

No. 20158
Sunny Character

■ This plan features:
— Three bedrooms
— Two and one half baths
■ A Kitchen with easy access to screened porch
■ A Master suite including walk-in closet and luxury bath
■ A second story balcony linking two bedrooms

FIRST FLOOR — 1,293 SQ. FT.
SECOND FLOOR — 526 SQ. FT.
BASEMENT — 1,286 SQ. FT.
GARAGE — 484 SQ. FT.

**TOTAL LIVING AREA:
1,819 SQ. FT.**

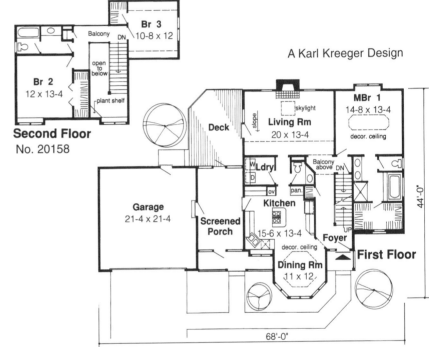

A Karl Kreeger Design

Second Floor
No. 20158

Br 3
10-8 x 12
Balcony
DN
open to below
Br 2
12 x 13-4
plant shelf

MBr 1
14-8 x 13-4
decor. ceiling
skylight
Living Rm
20 x 13-4
slope
Deck
Balcony above
DN
Ldry
W
D
ov
pan.
Kitchen
15-6 x 13-4
decor. ceiling
UP
Foyer
Garage
21-4 x 21-4
Screened Porch
Dining Rm
11 x 12
First Floor
44'-0"
68'-0"

No. 10596
Railing Divides Living Spaces

■ This plan features:
— Three bedrooms
— Two full baths

■ A one-level design with sunken, fireplaced Living Room

■ A wall of windows bringing natural light into two back bedrooms

■ An island Kitchen flowing easily into a sunny Breakfast Room

FIRST FLOOR — 1,740 SQ. FT.
BASEMENT — 1,377 SQ. FT.
GARAGE — 480 SQ. FT.

TOTAL LIVING AREA: 1,740 SQ. FT.

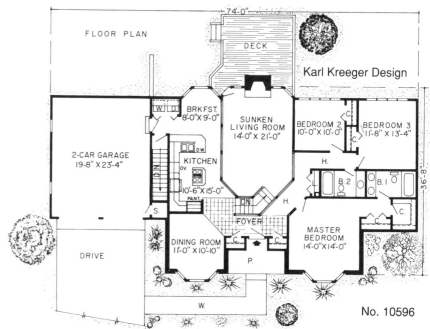

FLOOR PLAN

74'-0"

DECK

Karl Kreeger Design

BRKFST. 8'-0" X 9'-0"

SUNKEN LIVING ROOM 14'-0" X 21'-0"

BEDROOM 2 10'-0" X 10'-0"

BEDROOM 3 11'-8" X 13'-4"

2-CAR GARAGE 19'-8" X 23'-4"

KITCHEN 10'-6" X 15'-0"

B. 2   B. 1

MASTER BEDROOM 14'-0" X 14'-0"

DINING ROOM 11'-0" X 10'-10"

FOYER

DRIVE

36'-8"

W.

No. 10596

No. 10752
Living Areas Warmed by Massive Fireplace

■ This plan features:
— Three bedrooms
— Two full and one half bath

■ Skylights, sloping ceilings, and the absence of walls, giving the active areas an irresistible spacious atmosphere

■ A Living Room with a floor-to-ceiling window wall

■ A Dining Room with French doors

■ All bedrooms with walk-in closets

■ A large Master Suite with a private bath

FIRST FLOOR — 1,890 SQ. FT.
GARAGE — 488 SQ. FT.

TOTAL LIVING AREA: 1,890 SQ. FT.

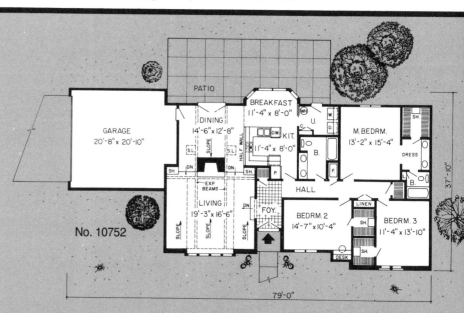

PATIO

GARAGE 20'-8" X 20'-10"

DINING 14'-6" X 12'-8"

BREAKFAST 11'-4" X 8'-0"

KIT. 11'-4" X 8'-0"

M. BEDRM. 13'-2" X 15'-4"

DRESS

EXP. BEAMS

LIVING 19'-3" X 16'-6"

HALL

FOY.

BEDRM. 2 14'-7" X 10'-4"

LINEN

BEDRM. 3 11'-4" X 13'-10"

DESK

No. 10752

37'-10"

79'-0"

No. 90663
Circular Staircase Makes Stunning Impression

■ This plan features:
— Four bedrooms
— Two full baths

■ A sunny well-equipped Kitchen efficiently located near the Dinette and formal Dining Room

■ A spacious fireplaced Family Room

■ A bow window dressing up the Living Room and making it seem larger

■ A Master Suite with a walk-in closet and private Master Bath

FIRST FLOOR — 1,119 SQ. FT.
SECOND FLOOR — 837 SQ. FT.
BASEMENT — 1,080 SQ. FT.

TOTAL LIVING AREA: 1,956 SQ. FT.

FIRST FLOOR PLAN

SECOND FLOOR PLAN

No. 90158
Compact Plan Allows for Gracious Living

■ This plan features:
— Three bedrooms
— Two full baths

■ A Great Room, accessible from the Foyer, offering cathedral ceilings, exposed beams, and a brick fireplace

■ A Kitchen with a center island and cathedral ceiling, accented by a round-top window

■ A Master Bedroom with a full bath and a walk-in closet

■ An optional basement, slab or crawl space foundation — please specify when ordering

MAIN AREA — 1,540 SQ. FT.
BASEMENT — 1,540 SQ. FT.

TOTAL LIVING AREA:
1,540 SQ. FT.

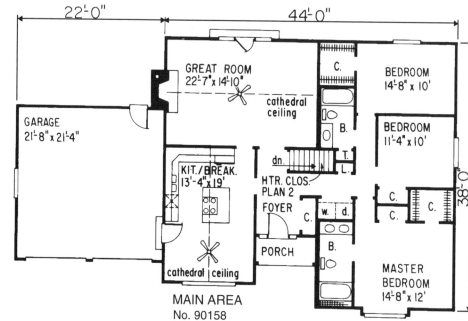

MAIN AREA
No. 90158

No. 93222
For an Established Neighborhood

■ This plan features:
— Three bedrooms
— Two full baths

■ A covered entrance sheltering and welcoming visitors

■ An expansive Living Room enhanced by natural light streaming in from the large front window

■ A bayed formal Dining Room with direct access to the Sun Deck and the Living Room for entertainment ease

■ A large Master Suite equipped with a walk-in closet and a full private Bath

■ Two additional bedrooms that share a full hall bath

MAIN AREA — 1,276 SQ. FT.
FINISHED STAIRCASE — 16 SQ. FT.
BASEMENT — 392 SQ. FT.
GARAGE — 728 SQ. FT.

No. 93222

TOTAL LIVING AREA:
1,292 SQ. FT.

A Jannis Vann & Associates, Inc. Design

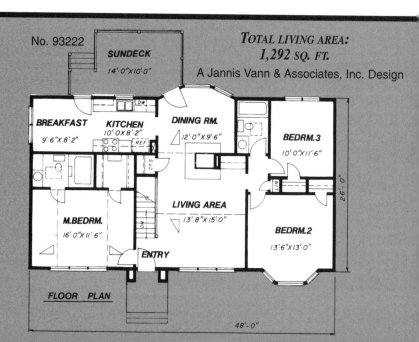

FLOOR PLAN

No. 92504
Traditional Elegance

■ This plan features:
— Four bedrooms
— Three and one half baths

■ A elegant entrance leading into a two story Foyer with an impressive staircase highlighted by a curved window

■ Floor to ceiling windows in both the formal Living and Dining Rooms

■ A spacious Den with a hearth fireplace, built-in book shelves, a wetbar and a wall of windows viewing the backyard

■ A large, efficient Kitchen, equipped with lots of counter and storage space, a bright Breakfast area, and access to the Dining Room, Utility Room, walk-in pantry and Garage

■ A grand Master Suite with decorative ceilings, a private Porch, an elaborate Bath and two walk-in closets

■ Three additional bedrooms on the second floor with walk-in closets, sharing adjoining, full baths and a ideal Children's Den

FIRST FLOOR — 2,553 SQ. FT.
SECOND FLOOR — 1,260 SQ. FT.
GARAGE — 714 SQ. FT.

No. 92504

FIRST FLOOR PLAN

SECOND FLOOR PLAN

TOTAL LIVING AREA:
3,813 SQ. FT.

No. 90971

Amenities Galore and Room to Grow

■ This plan features:

— Three bedrooms (future five)

— Two full baths (future three)

■ A front door Porch that shelters your arrival and adds a traditional flavor

■ A Foyer stairway that ascends to a truly unique and spacious Living/Dining Room graced by a gas fireplace and views from both front bay window and rear sliding glass doors to the covered Deck

■ An L-shaped Kitchen complete with built-in pantry, double sink, and a convenient snack bar for informal meals

■ A Covered Sun Deck accessed by both Kitchen and Dining Room extending entertainment possibilities

■ A large Master Suite with a walk-in closet and private full Bath

■ A basement ready to finish into a spacious Family Room, two additional bedrooms, and a bath/utility room

A Westhome Planners, Ltd. Design

MAIN AREA — 1,269 SQ. FT.
BASEMENT — 1,034 SQ. FT.
GARAGE — 462 SQ. FT.
COVERED PORCH — 140 SQ. FT.
WIDTH — 46'-0"
DEPTH — 41'-0"

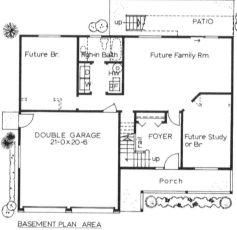

BASEMENT PLAN AREA

No. 90971

TOTAL LIVING AREA: 1,269 SQ. FT.

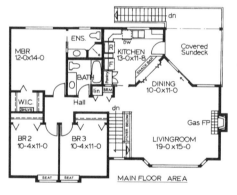

MAIN FLOOR AREA

No. 92509

Arched Windows Accent Sophisticated Design

■ This plan features:

— Four bedrooms

— Two full and one half baths

■ Graceful columns and full-length windows highlight front t Porch leading into central Foyer flanked by formal Living and Dining rooms

■ Spacious Great Room with decorative ceiling over hearth fireplace between built-in cabinets and sliding glass door to covered back Porch

■ Efficient Kitchen with peninsula counter, Breakfast alcove and adjoining Dining Room, Utility room and Garage

■ Secluded Master Bedroom suite offers access to back Porch, decorative ceiling and plush bath with walk-in closet, double vanity and spa tub

■ Three additional bedrooms with loads of closets space share double vanity bath

MAIN FLOOR — 2,551 SQ. FT.
GARAGE — 484 SQ. FT.
FOUNDATION — SLAB OR CRAWL SPACE

TOTAL LIVING AREA: 2,551 SQ. FT.

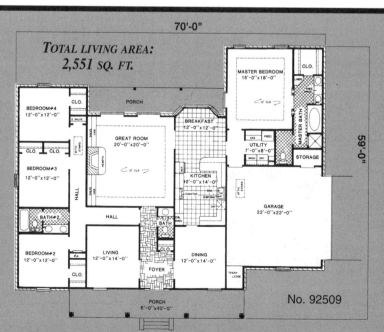

No. 92509

No. 91033
Neat and Tidy

■ This plan features:

— Two bedrooms

— Two full baths

■ A two story Living Room and Dining Room with a handsome stone fireplace

■ A well-appointed Kitchen with a peninsula counter

■ A Master Suite with a walk-in closet and private Master Bath

■ A large utility room with laundry facilities

■ An optional basement or crawl space foundation — please specify when ordering

FIRST FLOOR — 952 SQ. FT.

SECOND FLOOR — 297 SQ. FT.

TOTAL LIVING AREA:
1,249 SQ. FT.

No. 91033

OPEN TO DINING

LOFT

STORAGE

DN.

MSTR. BD
16/0x18/0

OPEN TO LIVING

STORAGE

UPPER FLOOR PLAN

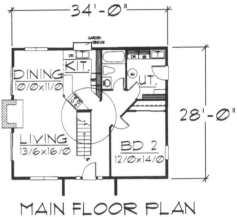

34'-0"

GARDEN WINDOW

DINING
10/0x11/0

KIT.

UT.

LIVING
13/6x16/0

BD 2
12/0x14/0

28'-0"

MAIN FLOOR PLAN

OPTIONAL
BASEMENT PLAN

No. 24311
Room for More

- This plan features:
- — Two bedrooms
- — Two full baths
- A Living Room with a fireplace and access to two decks, expanding the outdoor living space
- An efficient Kitchen opening to the Dining area
- A Master Bedroom, including a private bath with a corner spa/tub

MAIN AREA — 1,127 SQ. FT.

TOTAL LIVING AREA:
1,127 SQ. FT.

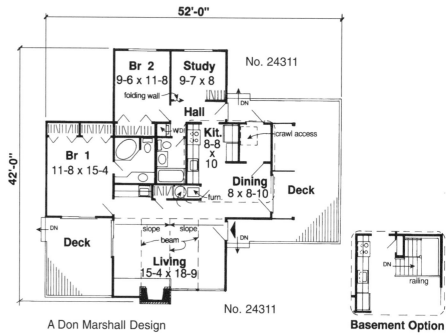

No. 24311

A Don Marshall Design

Basement Option

No. 26744
Cozy Contemporary Cape

- This plan features:
- — Three bedrooms
- — Two full and one half baths
- A sheltered entrance leading into a spacious Entry and a Living Room with a sloped ceiling and a stacked front window
- A well-appointed Kitchen serving the Breakfast area and the formal Dining Room with ease
- The Family Room offers a cozy fireplace flanked by windows and easy access to the outdoors
- A second floor Master Bedroom featuring a walk-in closet and a private bath
- Two additional bedrooms sharing a full hall bath and a Laundry area

FIRST FLOOR — 1,151 SQ. FT.
SECOND FLOOR — 893 SQ. FT.
BASEMENT — 1,047 SQ. FT.
GARAGE — 493 SQ. FT.

TOTAL LIVING AREA:
2,044 SQ. FT.

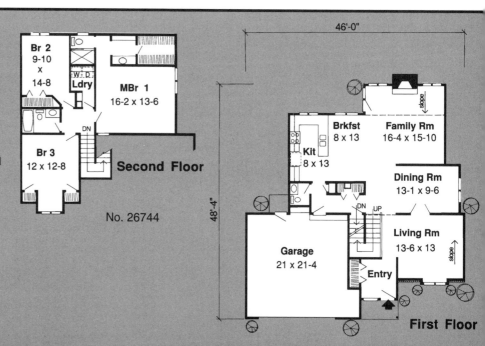

No. 26744

Second Floor

First Floor

No. 22020
Tasteful Elegance Aim of Design

■ This plan features:
— Three bedrooms
— Two full baths
■ A charming French Provincial exterior
■ A semi-circular Dining area overlooking the patio
■ An island Kitchen efficiently designed with ample cabinets and counter areas
■ A Family Room with a wood-burning fireplace
■ A Master Bedroom with a dressing area and a private bath

FIRST FLOOR — 1,772 SQ. FT.
GARAGE — 469 SQ. FT.

TOTAL LIVING AREA: 1,772 SQ. FT.

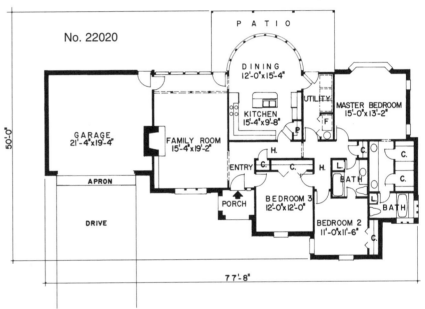

No. 22020

PATIO

DINING 12'-0"x15'-4"

KITCHEN 15'-4"x9'-8"

UTILITY

MASTER BEDROOM 15'-0"x13'-2"

GARAGE 21'-4"x19'-4"

FAMILY ROOM 15'-4"x19'-2"

ENTRY

BATH

BEDROOM 3 12'-0"x12'-0"

BEDROOM 2 11'-0"x11'-6"

BATH

APRON

PORCH

DRIVE

50'-0"

77'-8"

No. 90165
An Energy Efficient Home

■ This plan features:
— Three bedrooms
— Two full baths
■ A step-saving ranch layout with the bedrooms situated on one side of the home
■ A U-shaped Kitchen equipped with a peninsula counter/eating bar, double sink, and laundry area
■ A Great Room that may include a fireplace, open to the Dining Area enhancing spaciousness
■ A roomy Master Bedroom equipped with a walk-in closet and private Bath
■ Two additional bedrooms, one as a Den possibility, that share a full hall bath

MAIN AREA — 1,605 SQ. FT.

TOTAL LIVING AREA:
1,605 SQ. FT.

MAIN AREA
No. 90165

No. 90847
Versatile Chalet

■ This plan features:
— Two bedrooms
— Two full baths
■ A Sun deck entry into a spacious Living Room/Dining Room with a fieldstone fireplace, a large window and a sliding glass door
■ A well-appointed Kitchen with extended counter space and easy access to the Dining Room and the Utility area
■ A first floor bedroom adjoins a full hall bath
■ A spacious Master Bedroom, with a private Deck, a Suite bath and plenty of storage

FIRST FLOOR — 864 SQ. FT.
SECOND FLOOR — 496 SQ. FT.
WIDTH — 27' - 0"
DEPTH — 32' - 0"

TOTAL LIVING AREA:
1,360 SQ. FT.

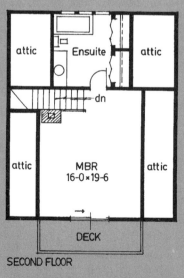

SECOND FLOOR

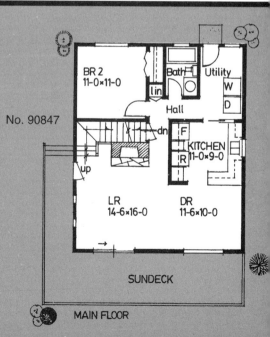

No. 90847

A Westhome Planners, Ltd. Design

No. 90697
Carefree Contemporary

■ This plan features:
— Three bedrooms
— Two full baths

■ A corner fireplace adding intrigue to the sunny Living Room

■ Skylights in the high sloping ceiling of the Family Room, which also has a greenhouse bay window and a heat-circulating fireplace

■ An elegant formal Dining Room with a window alcove

■ A Master Bedroom with a private Master Bath and two closets

■ Two additional bedrooms which share a full hall bath

MAIN AREA — 1,597 SQ. FT.
BASEMENT — 1,512 SQ. FT.

TOTAL LIVING AREA:
1,597 SQ. FT.

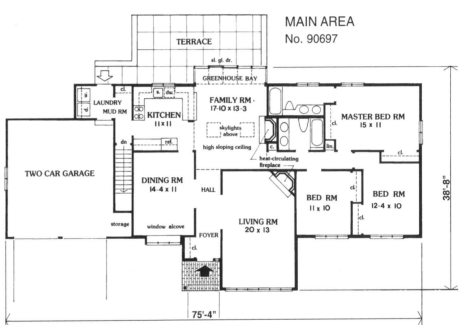

MAIN AREA
No. 90697

TERRACE

sl. gl. dr.

GREENHOUSE BAY

FAMILY RM.
17-10 x 13-3

MASTER BED RM
15 x 11

skylights
above

high sloping ceiling

heat-circulating
fireplace

LAUNDRY
MUD RM

KITCHEN
11 x 11

TWO CAR GARAGE

dn

ref.

DINING RM
14-4 x 11

HALL

BED RM
11 x 10

BED RM
12-4 x 10

storage

window alcove

LIVING RM
20 x 13

FOYER

cl.

75'-4"

38'-8"

No. 10778
Balcony Offers Sweeping Views

■ This plan features:
— Three bedrooms
— Three and one half baths

■ A Living Room and a formal Dining Room located off the foyer

■ A convenient island Kitchen steps away from both the Dining Room and the Three Season Porch

■ A cozy Master Suite including a fireplace and large a bath area

FIRST FLOOR — 1,978 SQ. FT
SECOND FLOOR — 1,768 SQ. FT.
BASEMENT — 1,978 SQ. FT.

TOTAL LIVING AREA:
3,746 SQ. FT.

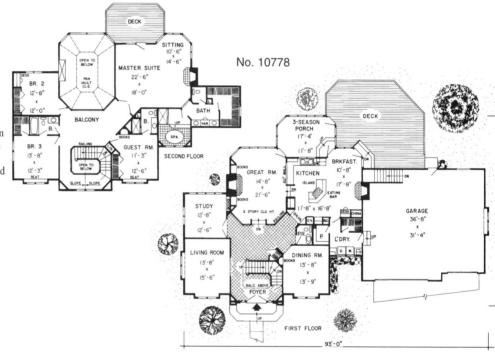

No. 10778

SITTING
10'-6"
x
14'-6"

MASTER SUITE
22'-6"
x
18'-0"

OPEN TO BELOW

PAN VAULT CLG.

DESK
BR. 2
12'-8"
x
12'-0"

BALCONY

BATH

B.

BR. 3
13'-8"
x
12'-3"
SEAT

RAILING

OPEN TO BELOW

BOOKS

GUEST RM.
11'-3"
x
12'-6"
SEAT

B.

SPA

VAN.

UP

SLOPE SLOPE

SECOND FLOOR

DECK

3-SEASON PORCH
17'-4"
x
11'-8"

BRKFAST.
10'-4"
x
17'-8"

KITCHEN
ISLAND

EATING BAR

11'-8" x 16'-8"

GREAT RM.
14'-8"
x
21'-6"

BOOKS

BOOKS

STUDY
12'-8"
x
12'-6"

2 STORY CLG. HT.

LIVING ROOM
13'-8"
x
15'-6"

BALC. ABOVE.

FOYER

UP

DESK
CHINA

PR.

P.

L'DRY.

D.
W.

DINING RM.
13'-8"
x
13'-9"

BOOKS

GARAGE
36'-8"
x
31'-4"

DN

UP

FIRST FLOOR

93'-0"

No. 24303
Affordable Living

■ This plan features:
— Three bedrooms
— Two full baths

■ A simple, yet gracefully designed exterior

■ A sheltered entrance into a roomy Living Room graced with a large front window

■ A formal Dining Room flowing from the Living Room, allowing for ease in entertaining

■ A well-appointed U-shaped Kitchen with double sinks and adequate storage

■ A Master Bedroom equipped with a full Bath

■ Two additional bedrooms that share a full hall bath complete with a convenient laundry center

■ A covered Patio, tucked behind the garage, perfect for a cook out or picnic

MAIN AREA — 984 SQ. FT.
BASEMENT — 860 SQ. FT.
GARAGE — 280 SQ. FT.
OPT. 2-CAR GARAGE — 400 SQ. FT.

54'-0"

MBr 1
13-7 x 11-8

Kit
8 x 8-3

Dining
8-10
x
8-3

Patio

W
D

a/c

Br 2
9-8
x
11-8

Br 3
11 x 10-2

Living Rm
15-8 x 11-7

Garage
13-9 x 19-4

28'-0"

driveway

No. 24303

Kit.
8 x 8-3

DN

1/2 wall

Basement Option

TOTAL LIVING AREA:
984 SQ. FT.

A Marshall Associates Design

178

No. 20069
Stylish and Practical Plan

■ This plan features:
— Three bedrooms
— Two and one half baths

■ A Kitchen with a Breakfast Area large enough for most informal meals

■ A spacious Living Room with a fireplace

■ A formal Dining Room with a decorative ceiling for comfortable entertaining

■ A first floor Master Bedroom providing a private retreat and lavish Master Bath

First Floor — 1,340 sq. ft.
Second floor — 651 sq. ft.
Basement — 1,322 sq. ft.

Total living area:
1,991 sq. ft.

No. 20069

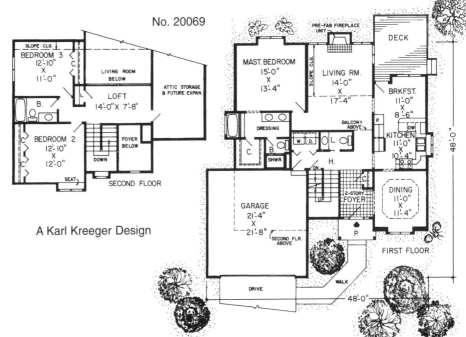

A Karl Kreeger Design

No. 10583
Loft Overlooks Foyer

■ This plan features:

— Four bedrooms

— Three full baths

■ Enormous rooms and two Garages

■ An island Kitchen with an eating peninsula for informal dining

■ A sun-filled Great Room with a massive fireplace and open-beamed ceiling

■ A large wrap-around deck to expand the outdoor living area

■ A Master Bedroom suite with a private deck, two large walk-in closets, and a lavish sky-lit tub

■ A large Recreation Room on the lower floor with access to the rear patio

FIRST FLOOR — 2,367 SQ. FT.

LOWER FLOOR — 1,241 SQ. FT.

BASEMENT (UNFINISHED) — 372 SQ. FT.

LOFT — 295 SQ. FT.

GARAGE (UPPER) — 660 SQ. FT.

GARAGE (LOWER) — 636 SQ. FT.

TOTAL LIVING AREA: 3,903 SQ. FT.

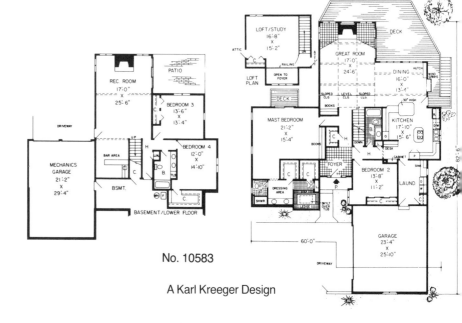

No. 10583

A Karl Kreeger Design

No. 20061
Options Abound

■ This plan features:

— Three bedrooms

— Two full baths

■ A striking exterior featuring vertical siding, shake shingles, and stone

■ A Kitchen with built-in pantry and appliances

■ An open beamed Master Bedroom

FIRST FLOOR — 1,674 SQ. FT.

BASEMENT — 1,656 SQ. FT.

GARAGE — 472 SQ. FT.

TOTAL LIVING AREA: 1,674 SQ. FT.

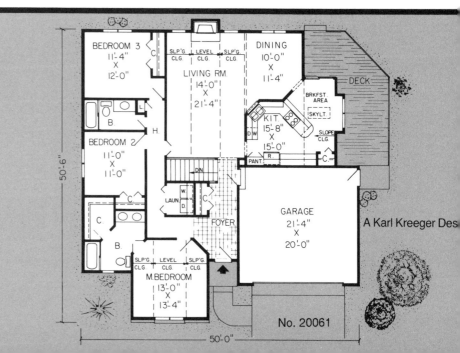

A Karl Kreeger Des

No. 20061

No. 20365
One-of-a-Kind

- This plan features:
  — Three bedrooms
  — Two and a half baths
- A porch sheltering the entry
- A fireplaced Dining Room with warmth and atmosphere
- A corner fireplace adding a focal point to the Parlor
- An island Kitchen with a Breakfast area and walk-in pantry

FIRST FLOOR — 955 SQ. FT.
SECOND FLOOR — 864 SQ. FT.
BASEMENT — 942 SQ. FT.

TOTAL LIVING AREA:
1,819 SQ. FT.

Second Floor

MBr 1
12-4 x 15

Br 3
12-10 x 13

No. 20365

Br 2
13 x 10-4

First Floor

pan.

Brkfst
10 x 9

Kit

china cab.

sink

Dining Rm
13 x 13-2

open to above

Entry

UP

Piazza

Parlor
15-4 x 13

40'-0"

41'-0"

No. 90966
Stately Manor

- This plan features:
— Three bedrooms
— Two full and one half baths
- A porch serving as a grand entrance
- A very spacious Foyer with an open staircase and lots of angles
- A beautiful Kitchen equipped with a cook top island and a full bay window wall that includes a roomy Breakfast Nook
- A Living Room with a vaulted ceiling that flows into the formal Dining Room for ease in entertaining
- A grand Master Suite equipped with a walk-in closet and five-piece private bath

FIRST FLOOR — 1,383 SQ. FT.
SECOND FLOOR — 997 SQ. FT.
BASEMENT — 1,374 SQ. FT.
GARAGE — 420 SQ. FT.
WIDTH — 54'-0"
DEPTH — 47'-0"

TOTAL LIVING AREA:
2,380 SQ. FT.

A Westhome Planners, Ltd. Design

SECOND FLOOR

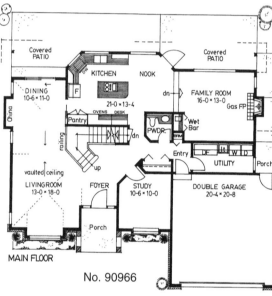

MAIN FLOOR

No. 90966

No. 92516
Distinctive European Design

- This plan features:
— Three bedrooms
— Two full baths
- A spacious Foyer leading into a grand Living Room, topped by a vaulted ceiling, with a fireplace between built-in cabinets and a wall of glass leading to a covered Porch
- A gourmet Kitchen with a peninsula counter/snackbar and a built-in pantry, that is central to the Dining Room, the bay window Breakfast area, the Utility Room and the Garage
- A large Master Bedroom, crowned by a raised ceiling, with French doors leading to a covered Porch, a luxurious bath and a walk-in closet
- Two additional bedrooms with decorative windows and over-sized closets share a full hall bath

MAIN FLOOR — 1,887 SQ. FT.
GARAGE & STORAGE — 524 SQ. FT.

TOTAL LIVING AREA:
1,887 SQ. FT.

MAIN AREA
No. 92516

No. 93227
Impressive Stone and Stucco

■ This plan features:
— Three bedrooms
— Two full and one half baths
■ Keystone entrance into central Foyer with gracefully curved staircase
■ Living Room with decorative window and hearth fireplace opens to Dining Room for easy entertaining
■ Hub Kitchen convenient to formal Dining Room, Breakfast area and Deck through atrium door, Laundry and Garage
■ Spacious Master Bedroom with walk-in closet and double vanity Master Bath
■ Two additional bedrooms with ample closets share a full bath
■ Bonus Room offers many options

FIRST FLOOR — 831 SQ. FT.
SECOND FLOOR — 810 SQ. FT.
BASEMENT —816 SQ. FT.
GARAGE — 484 SQ. FT
FOUNDATION —
BASEMENT, SLAB OR CRAWL SPACE

TOTAL LIVING AREA:
1,641 SQ. FT.

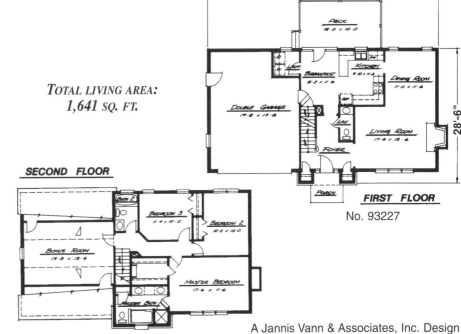

SECOND FLOOR

FIRST FLOOR
No. 93227

A Jannis Vann & Associates, Inc. Design

No. 92503
Charming Southern Traditional

■ This plan features:
— Three bedrooms
— Two full baths

■ A covered front porch with striking columns, brick quoins, and dentil molding

■ A spacious Great Room with vaulted ceilings, a fireplace, and built-in cabinets

■ A Utility Room adjacent to the Kitchen which leads to the   two- car Garage and Storage Rooms

■ A Master Bedroom including a large walk-in closet and a compartmentalized bath

MAIN AREA — 1,271 SQ. FT.

GARAGE — 506 SQ. FT.

TOTAL LIVING AREA:
1,271 SQ. FT.

MAIN AREA
No. 92503

No. 90991
Open Plan Brightens Elegant Traditional

■ This plan features:
— Three bedrooms
— Three full baths

■ A combination Family Room, Nook and Kitchen area that is over thirty-three feet in length

■ A very well-planned Kitchen with an island

■ A bay window in the Nook area

■ A Butler's Serving Pantry between the Kitchen and the Dining Room that includes an overhead cabinet with glass doors and a lower cabinet

■ A second floor Master Suite with a large walk-in closet and a private Master Bath with a whirlpool tub, separate shower and a double vanity

FIRST FLOOR — 1,173 SQ. FT.

SECOND FLOOR — 997 SQ. FT.

BASEMENT — 1,164 SQ. FT.

GARAGE — 574 SQ. FT.

WIDTH: 63' - 0"
DEPTH: 36' - 0"

TOTAL LIVING AREA:
2,170 SQ. FT.

A Westhome Planners, Ltd. Design

FIRST FLOOR
No. 90991

184

No. 91053
Updated Victorian

■ This plan features:
— Three bedrooms
— Two and a half baths

■ A classic Victorian exterior design accented by a wonderful turret room and second floor covered porch above a sweeping veranda

■ A spacious formal Living Room leading into a formal Dining Room for ease in entertaining

■ An efficient, U-shaped Kitchen with loads of counter space and a peninsula snackbar, opens to an eating Nook and Family Room for informal gatherings and activities

■ An elegant Master Suite with a unique, octagon Sitting area, a private Porch, an oversized, walk-in closet and private Bath with a double vanity and a window tub

■ Two additional bedrooms with ample closets sharing a full hall bath

FIRST FLOOR — 1,150 SQ. FT.
SECOND FLOOR — 949 SQ. FT.
GARAGE — 484 SQ. FT.

SECOND FLOOR

BEDRM • 2
13/10 x 10/0

BEDRM • 3
13/10 x 10/0

LINEN

MASTER BEDROOM
15/0 x 14/0 AVG.

W•I•C

B • 3

DN

SITTING

M • B

FRENCH

36" RAILING

TOTAL LIVING AREA:
2,099 SQ. FT.

No. 91053

FIRST FLOOR

DINING RM
11/0 x 13/0

KITCHEN
11/0 x 13/0

NOOK
9/0 x 9/0

FAMILY ROOM
15/0 x 12/0

UTIL

PANTRY

LIVING RM
17/6 x 13/8

PWDR

GARAGE
21/4 x 24/8

UP

35' - 0"

59' - 6"

No. 24304
Large Living in a Small Space

■ This plan features:
— Three bedrooms
— Two full baths

■ A sheltered entrance leads into an open Living Room with a corner fireplace and a wall of windows

■ A well-equipped Kitchen features a peninsula counter with a Nook, a laundry and clothes closet, and a built-in pantry

■ A Master Bedroom with a private bath

■ Two additional bedrooms that share full hall bath

MAIN FLOOR — 993 SQ. FT.
GARAGE — 987 SQ. FT.
OPTIONAL BASEMENT — 987 SQ. FT.

**TOTAL LIVING AREA:
993 SQ. FT.**

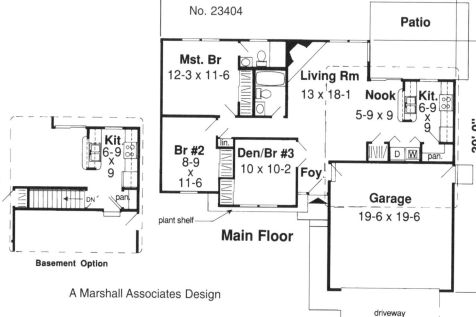

48'-0"

No. 23404

Patio

Mst. Br
12-3 x 11-6

Living Rm
13 x 18-1

Nook
5-9 x 9

Kit.
6-9 x 9

Br #2
8-9 x 11-6

Den/Br #3
10 x 10-2

Foy

Garage
19-6 x 19-6

39'-0"

plant shelf

Main Floor

driveway

Kit.
6-9 x 9

DN   pan.

Basement Option

A Marshall Associates Design

No. 90821
Vacation Cottage

■ This plan features:
— Two bedrooms
— One full bath

■ An economical, neat and simple design

■ Two picture windows in the Living/Dining Room

■ An efficient Kitchen design

■ A large, cozy loft bedroom flanked by big storage rooms

FIRST FLOOR — 616 SQ. FT.
LOFT — 180 SQ. FT.
WIDTH — 22'-0"
DEPTH — 28'-0"

**TOTAL LIVING AREA:
796 SQ. FT.**

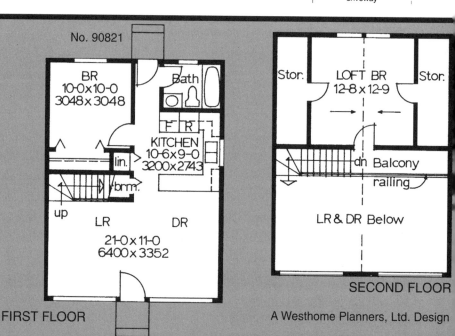

No. 90821

BR
10-0 x 10-0
3048 x 3048

Bath

KITCHEN
10-6 x 9-0
3200 x 2743

lin.

bm.

up

LR

DR

21-0 x 11-0
6400 x 3352

FIRST FLOOR

Stor.

LOFT BR
12-8 x 12-9

Stor.

dn **Balcony**
railing

LR & DR Below

SECOND FLOOR

A Westhome Planners, Ltd. Design

No. 90171
Versatile Chalet

■ This plan features:
— Three bedrooms
— One full bath

■ A rustic, shingled exterior giving a deep woods charm

■ A large Living Room, with a stone fireplace, joining the deck through sliding doors

■ An efficient Kitchen keeping cleanup to a minimum

■ An optional basement, crawl space or pier/beam foundation — please specify when ordering

FIRST FLOOR — 780 SQ. FT.
SECOND FLOOR — 500 SQ. FT.
BASEMENT — 780 SQ. FT.

TOTAL LIVING AREA:
1,280 SQ. FT.

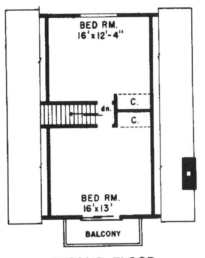

BED RM. 16'x12'-4"

dn. C. C.

BED RM. 16'x13'

BALCONY

SECOND FLOOR
No 90171

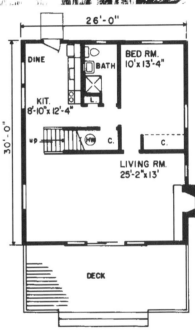

26'-0"

DINE
BATH
BED RM. 10'x13'-4"

KIT. 8'-10"x12'-4"

30'-0"

up HW C. C.

LIVING RM. 25'-2"x13'

DECK

FIRST FLOOR

No. 90992
A Main Floor Master Retreat

- This plan features:
  — Three bedrooms
  — Two full and one half baths
- An island Kitchen with a built-in pantry, desk, double sinks, as well as ample cabinet and counter space
- A bayed Nook area for informal eating
- A corner gas fireplace in the Family Room for that cozy touch
- A built-in china cabinet in the Dining Room
- A second gas fireplace in the expansive Living Room
- First floor Master Bedroom with a private Master Bath
- Two additional bedrooms, accented by dormers and window seats share a double vanity full bath
- Double garage has a workbench and an entry to both the Utility Room and the Lavatory

FIRST FLOOR — 1,306 SQ. FT.
SECOND FLOOR — 647 SQ. FT.
GARAGE — 504 SQ. FT.

TOTAL LIVING AREA: 1,953 SQ. FT.

SECOND FLOOR

A Westhome Planners, Ltd. Design

FIRST FLOOR
No. 90992

WIDTH 62'-0"
DEPTH 35'-6"

No. 93219
Old-Fashioned Country Porch

- This plan features:
  — Three bedrooms
  — Two full and one half baths
- A Living Area with a cozy fireplace visible from the Dining Room for warm entertaining
- A U-shaped, efficient Kitchen featuring a corner, double sink and pass-thru to the Dining Room
- A convenient half bath with a laundry center on the first floor
- A spacious, first floor Master Suite with a lavish Bath including a double vanity, walk-in closet and an oval, corner window tub
- Two large bedrooms with dormer windows, on the second floor, sharing a full hall bath

FIRST FLOOR — 1,057 SQ. FT.
SECOND FLOOR — 611 SQ. FT.
BASEMENT — 511 SQ. FT.
GARAGE — 546 SQ. FT.

TOTAL LIVING AREA: 1,668 SQ. FT.

A Jannis Vann & Associates, Inc. Design

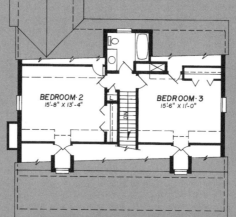

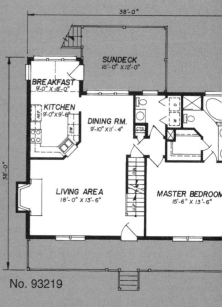

No. 93219

No. 92523
Private Master Suite

■ This plan features:
— Three bedrooms
— Two full baths

■ A spacious Great Room enhanced by a vaulted ceiling and fireplace

■ A well-equipped Kitchen with windowed double sink

■ A secluded Master Suite with decorative ceiling, private Master Bath, and walk-in closet

■ Two additional bedrooms sharing hall bath

FIRST FLOOR — 1,293 SQ. FT.

GARAGE — 400 SQ. FT.

TOTAL LIVING AREA: 1,293 SQ. FT.

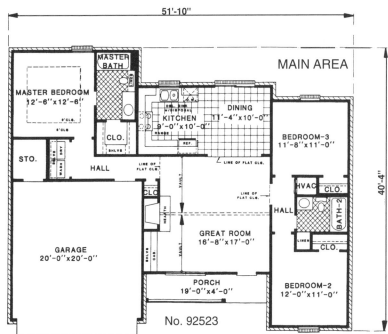

51'-10"

MAIN AREA

MASTER BATH

MASTER BEDROOM
12'-6''x12'-6''

CLO.

STO.

WASH DRY

HALL

CLO.

SHLVS

DBL. SINK W/DISPOSAL

KITCHEN
9'-0''x10'-0''

RANGE

REF.

DINING
11'-4''x10'-0''

LINE OF FLAT CLG.

LINE OF FLAT CLG.

LINE OF FLAT CLG.

VAULT

VAULT

HEARTH

SHLVS CAB

BEDROOM-3
11'-8''x11'-0''

HVAC

CLO.

HALL

BATH-2

LINEN

CLO.

GREAT ROOM
16'-8''x17'-0''

GARAGE
20'-0''x20'-0''

PORCH
19'-0''x4'-0''

BEDROOM-2
12'-0''x11'-0''

40'-4"

No. 92523

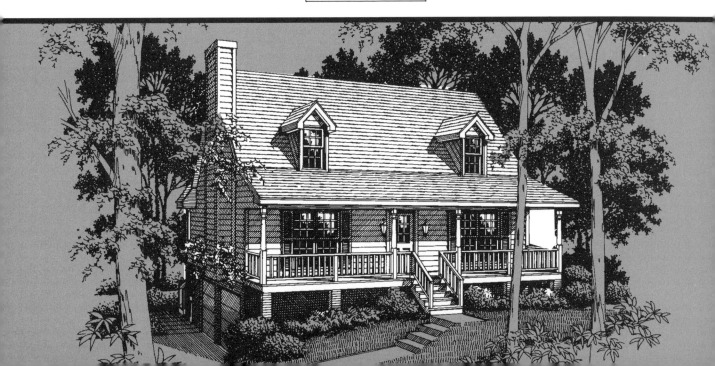

No. 20368
Spacious Stucco

■ This plan features:
— Three bedrooms
— Two and one half baths
■ A vaulted foyer flanked by a soaring Living Room with huge palladium windows
■ A Family Room with a massive two-way fireplace
■ A Master Suite with garden spa, private deck access, and a walk-in closet

FIRST FLOOR — 1,752 SQ. FT.
SECOND FLOOR — 620 SQ. FT.
BASEMENT — 1,726 SQ. FT.
GARAGE — 714 SQ. FT.

TOTAL LIVING AREA: 2,372 SQ. FT.

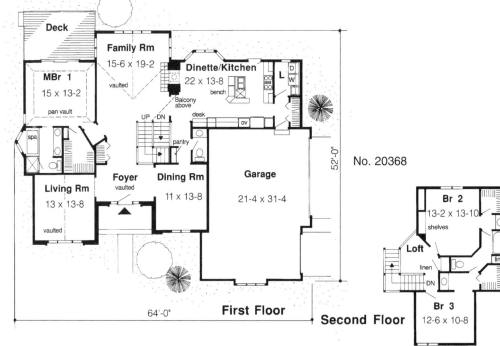

No. 20368

First Floor

- Deck
- Family Rm 15-6 x 19-2 (vaulted)
- Dinette/Kitchen 22 x 13-8 (bench)
- MBr 1 15 x 13-2 (pan vault)
- spa
- Balcony above
- UP DN
- desk
- pantry
- OV
- Living Rm 13 x 13-8 (vaulted)
- Foyer (vaulted)
- Dining Rm 11 x 13-8
- Garage 21-4 x 31-4
- 64'-0"
- 52'-0"

Second Floor

- Br 2 13-2 x 13-10 (shelves)
- Loft
- linen
- DN
- Br 3 12-6 x 10-8

No. 92525
Amenity-Packed Affordability

■ This plan features:
— Three bedrooms
— Two full baths
■ A sheltered entrance inviting your guests onward
■ A fireplace in the Den offering a focal point, while the decorative ceiling adds definition to the room
■ A well-equipped Kitchen flowing with ease into the Breakfast bay or Dining Room
■ A Master Bedroom, having two closets and a private Master Bath

MAIN AREA — 1,484 SQ. FT.

TOTAL LIVING AREA: 1,484 SQ. FT.

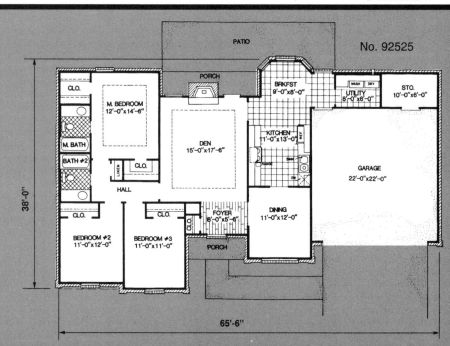

No. 92525

- PATIO
- PORCH
- CLO.
- M. BEDROOM 12'-0"x14'-6"
- BRKFST 9'-0"x8'-0"
- WASH DRY
- STO. 10'-0"x6'-0"
- M. BATH
- BATH #2
- KITCHEN 11'-0"x13'-0"
- UTILITY 8'-0"x6'-0"
- LINEN
- CLO.
- DEN 15'-0"x17'-6"
- GARAGE 22'-0"x22'-0"
- HALL
- CLO.
- CLO.
- CLO.
- FOYER 6'-0"x5'-6"
- DINING 11'-0"x12'-0"
- BEDROOM #2 11'-0"x12'-0"
- BEDROOM #3 11'-0"x11'-0"
- PORCH
- 38'-0"
- 65'-6"

No. 34047
A View from Every Room

■ This plan features:
— Three bedrooms
— Two and one half baths

■ A sunny, open atmosphere throughout the home

■ A two-story foyer flanked by a private study and a formal Living Room

■ A spacious Kitchen with a cook-top island, built-ins throughout, and a sink overlooking the rear patio

■ A glass-walled Breakfast area, three season porch, and the Family Room with a fireplace sharing a view of the backyard

■ A balcony overlooking the Family Room which links three spacious bedrooms and two full baths

■ A tremendous Master Suite with an abundance of closet space and a five-piece bath

FIRST FLOOR — 1,511 SQ. FT.
SECOND FLOOR — 1,163 SQ. FT.
BASEMENT — 1,511 SQ. FT.
GARAGE — 765 SQ. FT.

TOTAL LIVING AREA:
2,674 SQ. FT.

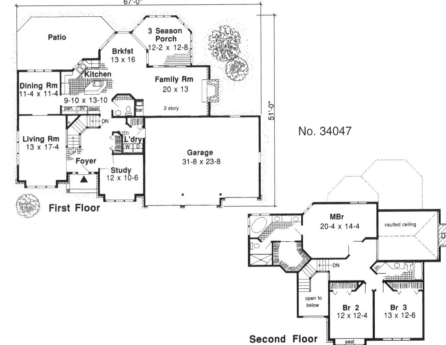

No. 34047

First Floor

- Patio
- 3 Season Porch 12-2 x 12-8
- Brkfst 13 x 16
- Kitchen 9-10 x 13-10
- Dining Rm 11-4 x 11-4
- Family Rm 20 x 13
- Living Rm 13 x 17-4
- L'dry
- Foyer
- Study 12 x 10-6
- Garage 31-8 x 23-8
- 67'-0"
- 51'-0"

Second Floor

- MBr 20-4 x 14-4
- vaulted ceiling
- open to below
- Br 2 12 x 12-4
- Br 3 13 x 12-6

No. 91774
Spacious Elegant Victorian

- This plan features:
  — Three bedrooms
  — Two and a half baths
- An attractive wrap-around porch leading to the Entry Hall
- A lovely bay window gracing the formal Living Room, which is highlighted by a fireplace
- A private, first floor Den equipped with built-in bookshelves
- A country Kitchen with a garden window, a Dining nook and double doors leading to the rear deck
- A classy Master Suite embracing a wide bay window, a romantic fireplace and a skylit bath
- Two additional bedrooms with private access to a full double vanity bath
- A Garage with a work area and a Kitchen entry

First floor — 1,315 sq. ft.
Second floor — 1,066 sq. ft.
Garage — 649 sq. ft.
Width — 72' - 0"
Depth — 34' - 0"

TOTAL LIVING AREA:
2,381 SQ. FT.

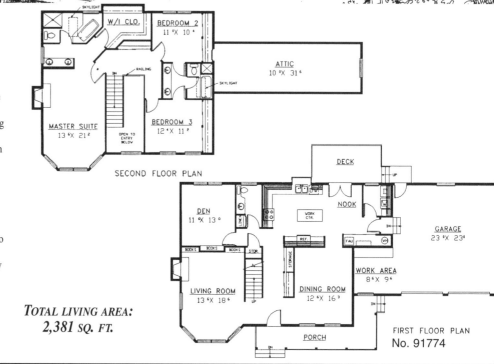

SECOND FLOOR PLAN

FIRST FLOOR PLAN
No. 91774

No. 92502
Spectacular Traditional

- This plan features:
  — Three bedrooms
  — Two full baths
- The use of gable roofs and the blend of stucco and brick to form a spectacular exterior
- A high vaulted ceiling and a cozy fireplace, with built-in cabinets in the Den
- An efficient, U-shaped Kitchen with an adjacent Dining Area
- A Master Bedroom, with a raised ceiling, that includes a private bath and a walk-in closet
- Two family bedrooms that share a full hall bath

MAIN AREA — 1,237 sq. ft.
GARAGE — 436 sq. ft.

TOTAL LIVING AREA:
1,237 SQ. FT.

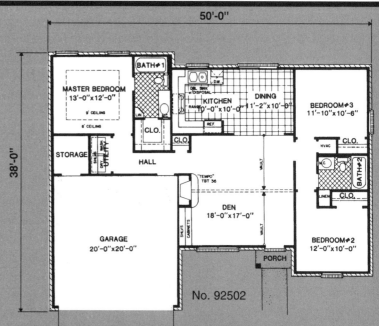

No. 92502

No. 90983
Attractive Roof Lines

■ This plan features:
— Three bedrooms
— Two full baths

■ An open floor plan shared by the sunken Living Room, Dining and Kitchen areas

■ An unfinished daylight Basement which will provide future bedrooms, a bathroom and laundry facilities

■ A Master Suite with a big walk-in closet and a private bath featuring a double shower

FIRST FLOOR — 1,396 SQ. FT.
BASEMENT — 1,396 SQ. FT.
GARAGE — 389 SQ. FT.
WIDTH — 48' - 0"
DEPTH — 54' - 0"

TOTAL LIVING AREA:
1,396 SQ. FT.

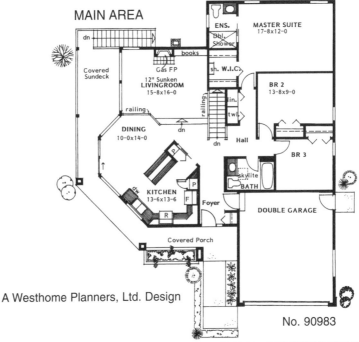

MAIN AREA

ENS.
Dbl. Shower
MASTER SUITE
17-8x12-0

dn
Covered Sundeck
books
Gas FP
sh. W.I.C.

12" Sunken
LIVINGROOM
15-8x16-0

BR 2
13-8x9-0

railing
lin.
twl
dn
Hall
dn

DINING
10-0x14-0

BR 3

skylite
BATH

KITCHEN
13-6x13-6

Foyer
DOUBLE GARAGE

Covered Porch

A Westhome Planners, Ltd. Design

No. 90983

No. 90178

Classic Ranch with Open Spaces

This plan features:

— Three bedrooms

— Two full and one half baths

■ A friendly Porch entry into a large Foyer with two closets and the Great Room beyond

■ An expansive Great Room with a Dining area, wet bar, fireplace and triple window view of property

■ An efficient, U-shaped Kitchen with a work island/snackbar, Breakfast area and sliding glass door to back yard, and next to the Mud Room and Garage entry

■ A corner Master Bedroom with tow walk-in closets, a sliding glass door to back yard and a double vanity Bath

■ Two additional bedrooms with ample closets, share a full bath

MAIN FLOOR — 2,705 SQ. FT.

GARAGE — 579 SQ. FT.

FOUNDATION — BASEMENT OR CRAWL SPACE

TOTAL LIVING AREA: 2,705 SQ. FT.

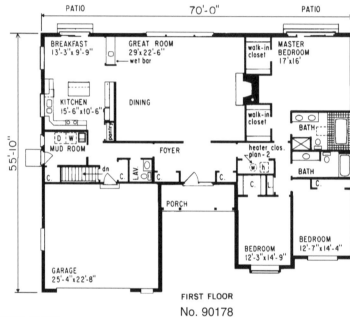

FIRST FLOOR
No. 90178

No. 34353

Classic Ranch Has Contemporary Flavor

■ This plan features:

— Three bedrooms

— Two full baths

■ A Galley-styled Kitchen easily serving the Dining Room

■ A Living Room with bump out window and fireplace

■ Ample closet space

■ A Master Bedroom with a private bath and an individual shower

FIRST FLOOR — 1,268 SQ. FT.

BASEMENT — 1,248 SQ. FT.

TOTAL LIVING AREA: 1,268 SQ. FT.

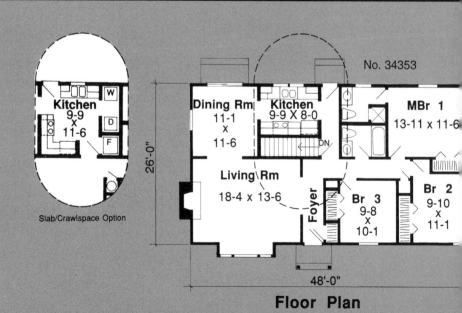

Slab/Crawlspace Option

No. 34353

Floor Plan

No. 10686
Every Luxurious Feature One Could Want

■ This plan features:
— Four bedrooms
— Two and one half baths

■ An open staircase leading to the bedrooms and dividing the space between the vaulted Living and Dining Rooms

■ A wide family area including the Kitchen, Dinette and Family Room complete with built-in bar, bookcases, and fireplace

■ A Master Bedroom with a vaulted ceiling, spacious closets and Jacuzzi

FIRST FLOOR — 1,786 SQ. FT.
SECOND FLOOR — 1,490 SQ. FT.
BASEMENT — 1,773 SQ. FT.
GARAGE — 579 SQ. FT.

TOTAL LIVING AREA: 3,276 SQ. FT.

SECOND FLOOR

No. 10686

FIRST FLOOR

No. 92527
Secluded Master Suite

■ This plan features:
— Three bedrooms
— Two full baths

■ A convenient one-level design with an open floor plan between the Kitchen, Breakfast area and Great Room

■ A vaulted ceiling and a cozy fireplace in the spacious Great Room

■ A well-equipped Kitchen using a peninsula counter as an eating bar

■ A Master Suite with a luxurious Master Bath

■ Two additional bedrooms having use of a full hall bath

MAIN AREA — 1,680 SQ. FT.

TOTAL LIVING AREA:
1,680 SQ. FT.

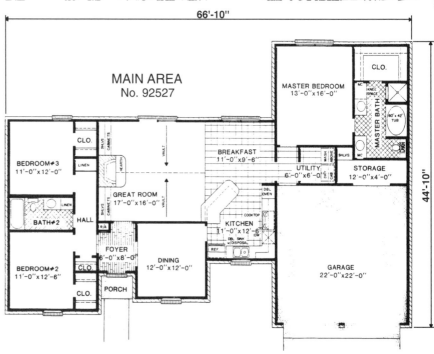

MAIN AREA
No. 92527

No. 93261
Bay Windows and a Terrific Front Porch

■ This plan features:
— Three bedrooms
— Two full baths

■ An expansive Living Area that includes a fireplace

■ A Master Suite with a private Master Bath and a walk-in closet, as well as a bay window view of the front yard

■ An efficient Kitchen that serves the sunny Breakfast Area and the Dining Room with equal ease

■ Two additional bedrooms that share the full hall bath

■ A convenient main floor Laundry Room

MAIN AREA — 1,778 SQ. FT.
BASEMENT — 1,008 SQ. FT.
GARAGE — 728 SQ. FT.

TOTAL LIVING AREA:
1,778 SQ. FT.

MAIN AREA
No. 93261

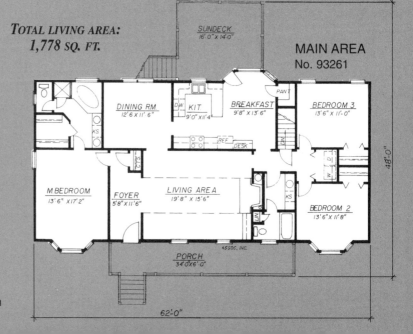

A Jannis Vann & Associates, Inc. Design

No. 90934
A Nest for Empty-Nesters

■ This plan features:
— Two bedrooms
— One full bath
■ An economical design
■ A covered sun deck adding outdoor living space
■ A mudroom/laundry area inside the side door, trapping dirt before it can enter the house
■ An open layout between the Living Room with fireplace, Dining Room and Kitchen

FIRST FLOOR — 884 SQ. FT.
WIDTH — 34'-0"
DEPTH — 28'-0"

TOTAL LIVING AREA:
884 SQ. FT.

A Westhome Planners, Ltd. Design

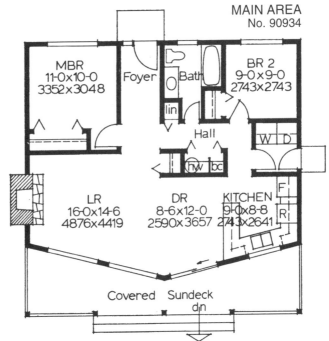

MAIN AREA
No. 90934

MBR
11-0x10-0
3352x3048

Foyer

Bath

BR 2
9-0x9-0
2743x2743

lin

Hall

W D

hw bc

LR
16-0x14-6
4876x4419

DR
8-6x12-0
2590x3657

KITCHEN
9-0x8-8
2743x2641

F
R

Covered   Sundeck
dn

No. 20068
Wonderful Views

■ This plan features:
— Three bedrooms
— Two and one half full baths
■ A fireplaced Living Room with sloped ceiling
■ A second floor balcony
■ A huge Master Bedroom featuring a lavish bath
■ Walk-in closets for all bedrooms

FIRST FLOOR — 1,266 SQ. FT.
SECOND FLOOR — 489 SQ. FT.
BASEMENT — 1,266 SQ. FT.
GARAGE — 484 SQ. FT.

TOTAL LIVING AREA:
1,755 SQ. FT.

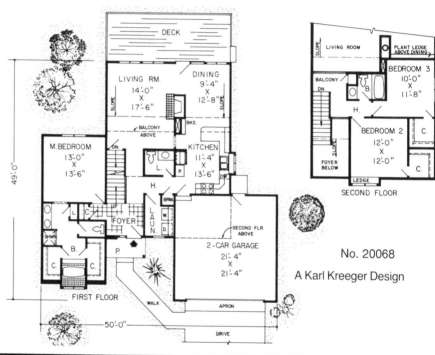

No. 20068

A Karl Kreeger Design

No. 20155
Built-in Beauty

■ This plan features:
— Four bedrooms
— Four and one half bath
■ An L-shaped Living and Dining Room arrangement with a fireplace flanked by bookcases and a decorative ceiling in the Dining area
■ A gourmet Kitchen with range-top island/snack bar, built-in pantry and double sinks
■ A massive fireplace with wood storage that separates the Hearth/Breakfast Room from the sky-lit Sun Room
■ A Master Suite with a decorative ceiling, walk-in closet, elegant bath and private access to the screened porch
■ Three additional bedrooms that share use of a full hall bath

FIRST FLOOR — 2,800 SQ. FT.
SECOND FLOOR — 1,113 SQ. FT.
BASEMENT — 2,800 SQ. FT.
SCREEN PORCH — 216 SQ. FT.
GARAGE — 598 SQ. FT.

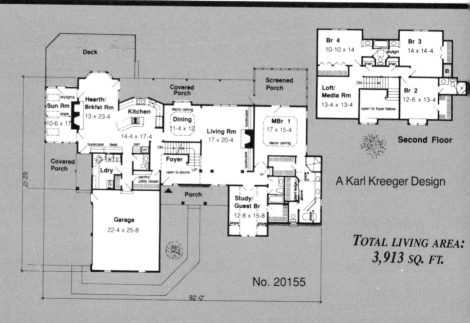

A Karl Kreeger Design

TOTAL LIVING AREA:
3,913 SQ. FT.

No. 20155

No. 20367
Clapboard Contemporary

■ This plan features:
— Three bedrooms
— Two and one half baths

■ An exciting window wall gracing the dramatic two-story Living Room

■ A Kitchen with double sink, built-in desk and easy access to Dining Room

■ A step down to sunken Family Room with fireplace

■ A Master Bedroom with luxurious Master Bath and unique balcony

FIRST FLOOR — 1,108 SQ. FT.
SECOND FLOOR — 786 SQ. FT.
BASEMENT — 972 SQ. FT.
GARAGE — 567 SQ. FT.

TOTAL LIVING AREA:
1,894 SQ. FT.

No. 20367

Second Floor

MBr 1 12 x 15-8	Br 2 12-2 x 10
	Br 3 11 x 11-2

open to below

First Floor

Deck
Kitchen 11-4 x 12-8
desk / bar
Family Rm 17 x 12-6
Dining Rm 12 x 11-6
line of floor above
Living Rm 15-6 x 12-6
slope / slope
Foyer
Garage 23-8 x 23-8
W D / L
39'-6"
52'-0"

No. 24319
Home With Many Views

- This plan features:
- — Three bedrooms
- — Two full baths
- Large Decks and windows taking full advantage of the view
- A fireplace that divides the Living Room from the Dining Room
- A Kitchen flowing into the Dining Room
- A Master Bedroom with full Master Bath
- A Recreation Room sporting a whirlpool tub and a bar

MAIN FLOOR — 728 SQ. FT.
UPPER FLOOR — 573 SQ. FT.
LOWER FLOOR — 379 SQ. FT.
GARAGE — 240 SQ. FT.

TOTAL LIVING AREA: 1,680 SQ. FT.

A Marshall Associates Design

No. 24319

No. 10657
Designed for Privacy

- This plan features:
- — Three bedrooms
- — Two and one half baths
- A Kitchen with a cooking island that opens to a Morning Room accessible to a deck and sunroom with a hot tub
- A Master Suite including a room-sized closet, double vanity and skylit tub with separate shower
- Ample room throughout, including the fireplaced Living Room and the formal Dining Room with recessed ceilings

FIRST FLOOR — 1,838 SQ. FT.
SECOND FLOOR — 798 SQ. FT.
BASEMENT — 1,831 SQ. FT.
GARAGE — 800 SQ. FT.

TOTAL LIVING AREA: 2,636 SQ. FT.

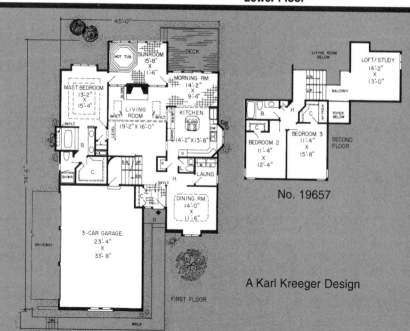

No. 19657

A Karl Kreeger Design

No. 26112
Contemporary Design Features Sunken Living Room

■ This plan features:

— Two bedrooms, with possible third bedroom/den

— One and one half baths

■ A solar design with southern glass doors, windows, and an air-lock entry

■ R-26 insulation used for floors and sloping ceilings

■ A deck rimming the front of the home

■ A Dining Room separated from the Living Room by a half wall

■ An efficient Kitchen with an eating bar

FIRST FLOOR — 911 SQ. FT.
SECOND FLOOR — 576 SQ. FT.
BASEMENT — 911 SQ. FT.

TOTAL LIVING AREA: 1,487 SQ. FT.

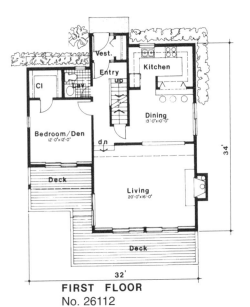

FIRST FLOOR
No. 26112

SECOND FLOOR

No. 20451
Dramatic Impressions

■ This plan features:

— Three bedrooms

— Two full and one half baths

■ A soaring Living Room off the vaulted, sky-lit Foyer

■ A cozy Family Room that shares the backyard view with the glass-walled Breakfast room

■ A Kitchen that easily serves every area, including the elegant, formal Dining Room at the front of the house

■ A Master Suite, tucked behind the garage, including private deck access, and a magnificent Bath with a garden tub

MAIN AREA — 2,084 SQ. FT.

TOTAL LIVING AREA:
2,084 SQ. FT.

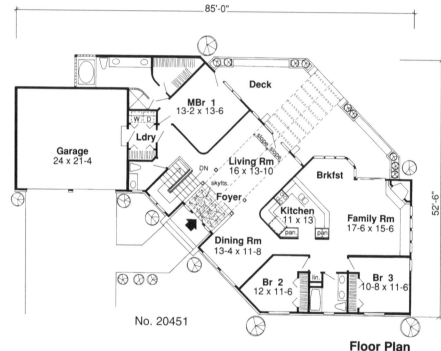

Floor Plan

No. 34681
Impressive Entry Crowned by Window

■ This plan features:

— Three bedrooms

— Two full and one half baths

■ Transom and sidelight windows crowning the entry door, adding natural light to the Foyer

■ A split Foyer entry, with a half flight of stairs leading down to the Family Room and Den with a full sized closet

■ A large Living Room adjoining the formal Dining Room, for convenience in entertaining

■ An efficient Kitchen that includes a double sink and direct access to the rear yard

■ A Master Bedroom equipped with a private full Bath

■ Two additional bedrooms that share the full hall Bath

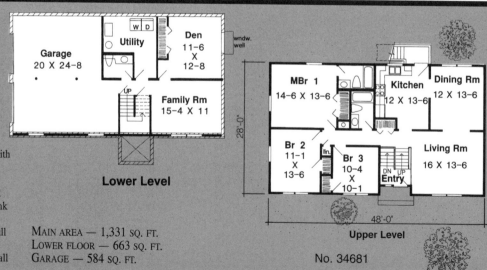

MAIN AREA — 1,331 SQ. FT.
LOWER FLOOR — 663 SQ. FT.
GARAGE — 584 SQ. FT.

TOTAL LIVING AREA:
1,994 SQ. FT.

No. 10683

Enjoy a Crackling Fire on a Chilly Day

- This plan features:
- — Three bedrooms
- — Two and one half baths
- A dramatic two-story entry
- Cathedral ceilings in both the Dining Room and the sunken Living Room
- An efficient corner Kitchen
- A sunken Great Room with a fireplace
- An angular staircase leading to the Master Bedroom

FIRST FLOOR — 990 SQ. FT.
SECOND FLOOR — 721 SQ. FT.
BASEMENT — 934 SQ. FT.
GARAGE — 429 SQ. FT.

TOTAL LIVING AREA: 1,711 SQ. FT.

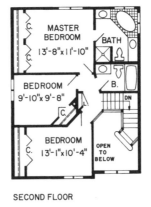

SECOND FLOOR

No. 10683

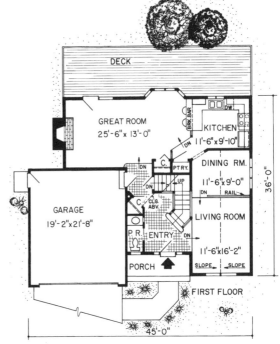

No. 10692
Plenty of Room for Everyone

This plan features:

— Five bedrooms

— Four full baths

■ A bright two-story Entry leads into formal Living Room with an inviting fireplace and graceful arched window below a sloped ceiling

■ A formal Dining Room highlighted by a decorative window and a butler's pantry leading to Kitchen

■ An efficient, U-shaped Kitchen with a serving bar for the Breakfast area, Family Room and covered Patio beyond

■ The open Family Room/Breakfast area with a cozy fireplace, bar area, book shelves and access to the Utility room and Garage with a Workshop

■ The private Master Bedroom wing offers a huge walk-in closet and a luxurious bath

■ Four bedrooms with ample closets, on the second floor share two double vanity baths and a Study

FIRST FLOOR — 2,313 SQ. FT.

SECOND FLOOR — 1,256 SQ. FT.

GARAGE — 662 SQ. FT.

FOUNDATION — SLAB ONLY

No. 10692

TOTAL LIVING AREA:
3,569 SQ. FT.

No. 20405
Past Luxuries Revisited

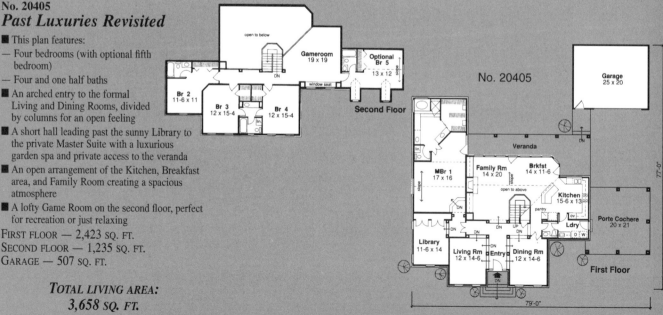

■ This plan features:

— Four bedrooms (with optional fifth bedroom)

— Four and one half baths

■ An arched entry to the formal Living and Dining Rooms, divided by columns for an open feeling

■ A short hall leading past the sunny Library to the private Master Suite with a luxurious garden spa and private access to the veranda

■ An open arrangement of the Kitchen, Breakfast area, and Family Room creating a spacious atmosphere

■ A lofty Game Room on the second floor, perfect for recreation or just relaxing

FIRST FLOOR — 2,423 SQ. FT.

SECOND FLOOR — 1,235 SQ. FT.

GARAGE — 507 SQ. FT.

TOTAL LIVING AREA:
3,658 SQ. FT.

204

No. 90682
Inviting Porch Adorns Affordable Home

■ This plan features:
— Three bedrooms
— Two full baths

■ A large and spacious Living Room that adjoins the Dining Room for ease in entertaining

■ A private bedroom wing offering a quiet atmosphere

■ A Master Bedroom with his-n-her closets and a private bath

■ An efficient Kitchen with a walk-in pantry

MAIN AREA — 1,160 SQ. FT.
LAUNDRY/MUDROOM — 83 SQ. FT.

TOTAL LIVING AREA:
1,243 SQ. FT.

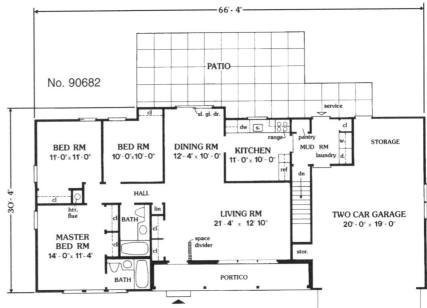

No. 90682

66'-4"

PATIO

service

BED RM
11'-0" x 11'-0"

BED RM
10'-0" x 10'-0"

DINING RM
12'-4" x 10'-0"

KITCHEN
11'-0" x 10'-0"

sl. gl. dr.

dw s.

range

pantry

MUD RM
laundry

cl

w.

d.

STORAGE

30'-4"

cl

htr. flue

HALL

BATH

lin

ref

dn

LIVING RM
21'-4" x 12'10"

TWO CAR GARAGE
20'-0" x 19'-0"

MASTER
BED RM
14'-0" x 11'-4"

cl

space divider

stor.

BATH

PORTICO

No. 84056
Convenient Single Level

■ This plan features:
— Three bedrooms
— Two full baths

■ A well-appointed U-shaped Kitchen that includes a view of the front yard and a built-in pantry

■ An expansive Great Room with direct access to the rear yard, expanding the living space

■ A Master Bedroom equipped with two closets—one is a walk-in, and a private bath

■ Two additional bedrooms that share a full hall bath

■ A step-saving, centrally located laundry center

FIRST FLOOR — 1,644 SQ. FT.
GARAGE — 576 SQ. FT.

**TOTAL LIVING AREA:
1,644 SQ. FT.**

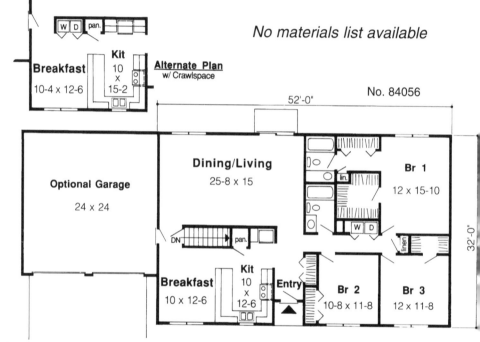

No materials list available

Kit
10 x 15-2

Breakfast
10-4 x 12-6

Alternate Plan
w/ Crawlspace

No. 84056

52'-0"

Optional Garage
24 x 24

Dining/Living
25-8 x 15

Br 1
12 x 15-10

32'-0"

Breakfast
10 x 12-6

Kit
10 x 12-6

Entry

Br 2
10-8 x 11-8

Br 3
12 x 11-8

No. 10483
Intelligent Use of Space

No. 10483

A Karl Kreeger Design

■ This plan features:
— Three bedrooms
— Two full baths

■ Lots of living packed into this well-designed home

■ A combined Kitchen and Dining Room

■ A highly functional Kitchen, including a corner sink under double windows

■ A Living Room accentuated by a large fireplace and well-placed skylight

■ A sleeping area containing three bedrooms and two full baths

MAIN AREA — 1,025 SQ. FT.
GARAGE — 403 SQ. FT.

**TOTAL LIVING AREA:
1,025 SQ. FT.**

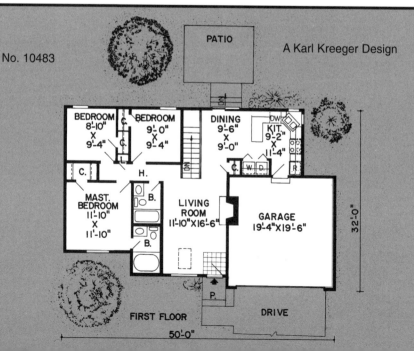

PATIO

BEDROOM
8'-10" X 9'-4"

BEDROOM
9'-0" X 9'-4"

DINING
9'-6" X 9'-0"

KIT.
9'-2" X 11'-4"

MAST. BEDROOM
11'-10" X 11'-10"

LIVING ROOM
11'-10"X16'-6"

GARAGE
19'-4"X19'-6"

32'-0"

FIRST FLOOR

DRIVE

50'-0"

No. 34827
Comfortable Family Home
Leaves Room to Grow

■ This plan features:
— Three bedrooms
— Two and one half baths

■ Formal Living and Dining Rooms off the central foyer for ease in entertaining

■ A Family Room with a large fireplace adjoining the Breakfast area with a bay window

■ A short hall leading past the powder room, linking the formal Dining Room with the Kitchen

■ Each bedroom containing a walk-in closet

■ A Master Suite including both a raised tub and a step-in shower

FIRST FLOOR — 1,212 SQ. FT.
SECOND FLOOR — 1,030 SQ. FT.
BASEMENT — 1,212 SQ. FT.
GARAGE — 521 SQ. FT.

**TOTAL LIVING AREA:
2,242 SQ. FT.**

No. 34827

No. 24308
Leisure Time Getaway

■ This plan features:
— One bedroom
— One full bath

■ The simplicity of an A-frame with a spacious feeling achieved by the large, two-story Living Room

■ An entrance deck leads into the open Living Room accented by a spiral staircase to the Loft

■ A small, but efficient Kitchen serves the Living area easily, and provides access to the full bath with a shower and a storage area

■ A first floor bedroom and a Loft area provide the sleeping quarters

FIRST FLOOR — 660 SQ. FT.
LOFT — 163 SQ. FT.

TOTAL LIVING AREA:
823 SQ. FT.

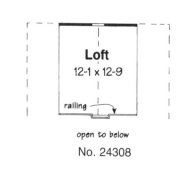

Loft
12-1 x 12-9

railing

open to below

No. 24308

A Marshall Associates Design

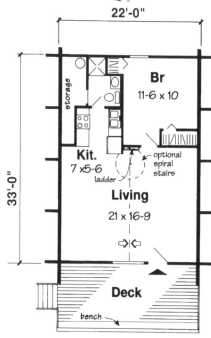

Main Floor

No. 10748
Outdoor-Lovers' Delight

■ This plan features:
— Three bedrooms
— Two full baths

■ A roomy Kitchen and Dining Room

■ A massive Living Room with a fireplace and access to the wrap-around porch via double French doors

■ An elegant Master Suite and two additional spacious bedrooms closely located to the laundry area

MAIN AREA — 1,540 SQ. FT.
PORCHES — 530 SQ. FT.

TOTAL LIVING AREA:
1,540 SQ. FT.

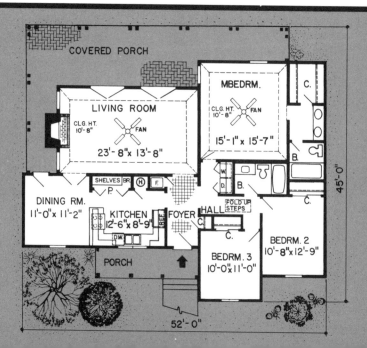

No. 10748

208

No. 20364
Lofty Views

■ This plan features:
— Three bedrooms
— Two and one half baths
■ A two-story foyer with lofty views
■ A spacious Living and Dining Room arrangement with vaulted ceilings
■ An efficient island Kitchen opening to a sunny Breakfast room with sliders to the rear patio
■ A Family Room with a large fireplace and views of the backyard
■ A Master Suite complete with a private bath

FIRST FLOOR — 1,060 SQ. FT.
SECOND FLOOR — 990 SQ. FT.
BASEMENT — 1,060 SQ. FT.
GARAGE — 462 SQ. FT.

TOTAL LIVING AREA:
2,050 SQ. FT.

MBr
14-10 x 14-2

Loft

open to below

DN

Br 3
10 x 13

Br 2
10 x 10-6

Second Floor

No. 20364

Patio   46'-0"

Family Rm
15 x 14

Brkfst
9 x 15-6

Kitchen
9 x 15-6

Dining Rm
11-6 x 12-6

desk   pan.
lin.

vaulted

38'-6"

Garage
20-8 x 20-8

Living Rm
11-6 x 12-6

DN   UP

Foyer

Porch

First Floor

No. 24317

Natural Light Creates Bright Living Spaces

■ This plan features:
— Three bedrooms
— Two full baths

■ A generous use of windows throughout the home, creating a bright living space

■ A center work island and a built-in pantry in the Kitchen

■ A sunny Eating Nook for informal eating and a formal Dining Room for entertaining

■ A large Living Room with a cozy fireplace to add atmosphere to the room as well as warmth

■ A Master Bedroom with a private bath and double closets

■ Two additional bedrooms that share a full, compartmented hall bath

MAIN AREA — 1,620 SQ. FT.

TOTAL LIVING AREA:
1,620 SQ. FT.

50'-0"

55'-8"

M Br 14 x 15
Living 13-10 x 21-5
Optional Patio
Br 2 12 x 11-2
linen
DN
railing
Dining 11-2 x 9
Den / Br 3 13 x 11-4
pantry
Kit.
D W
Garage 19-4 x 19-8
Nook 13-6 x 13
No. 24317
Main Floor

A Don Marshall Design

No. 34376

Charming Exterior Hints at Inviting Interior

■ This plan features:
— Three bedrooms
— Two full baths

■ An arched window and a covered porch entry

■ An open Living Room and Dining Room arrangement spanning the full depth of the home

■ A Kitchen, including a corner sink with a window overlooking the backyard

■ Twin bay windows adding light and space to the informal Dining area and Master Suite

■ An attached street-side Garage adding a sound buffer for the three bedrooms

FIRST FLOOR — 1,748 SQ. FT.
BASEMENT — 1,693 SQ. FT.
GARAGE — 541 SQ. FT.

TOTAL LIVING AREA:
1,748 SQ. FT.

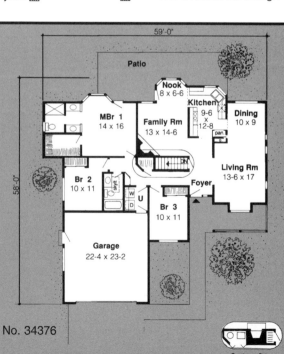

59'-0"
58'-0"
Patio
Nook 8 x 6-6
Kitchen 9-6 x 12-8
Dining 10 x 9
MBr 1 14 x 16
Family Rm 13 x 14-6
pan.
Living Rm 13-6 x 17
Br 2 10 x 11
W D
U
Br 3 10 x 11
Foyer
Garage 22-4 x 23-2
No. 34376
Crawlspace Option

No. 10531

Luxury is Always Popular

A Karl Kreeger Design

■ This plan features:
— Three bedrooms
— Three full and one half bath

■ A sunken Great Room, a spectacular Breakfast Nook, and a bridge-like balcony on the second floor

■ A Master Suite highlighted by two huge walk-in closets, a five-piece bath, and a sitting room with bay window

■ A Great Room accented by a bar, fireplace, and built-in cabinets for the television and stereo

■ Cathedral ceilings in the Dining Room and foyer

FIRST FLOOR — 2,579 SQ. FT.
SECOND FLOOR — 997 SQ. FT.
BASEMENT — 2,579 SQ. FT.
GARAGE & STORAGE — 1,001 SQ. FT.

TOTAL LIVING AREA:
3,576 SQ. FT.

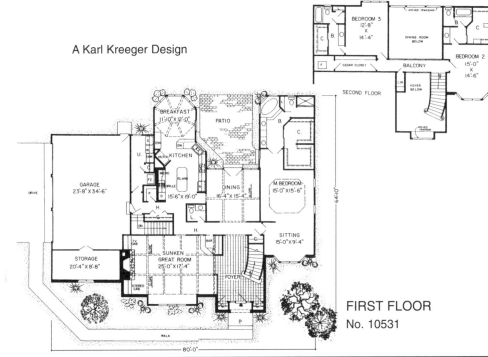

FIRST FLOOR
No. 10531

No. 34150
Simple Lines Enhanced by Elegant Window Treatment

■ This plan features:
— Two bedrooms (optional third)
— Two full baths

■ A huge, arched window that floods the front room with natural light

■ A homey, well-lit Office or Den

■ Compact, efficient use of space

■ An efficient Kitchen with easy access to the Dining Room

■ A fireplaced Living Room with a sloping ceiling and a window wall

■ A Master Bedroom sporting a private Master Bath with a roomy walk-in closet

FIRST FLOOR — 1,492 SQ. FT.
BASEMENT — 1,486 SQ. FT.
GARAGE — 462 SQ. FT.

TOTAL LIVING AREA:
1,492 SQ. FT.

A Karl Kreeger Design

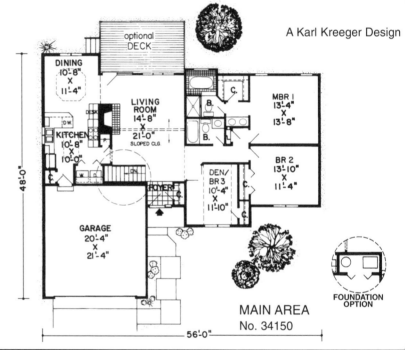

MAIN AREA
No. 34150

FOUNDATION OPTION

No. 90933
Tradition with a Twist

■ This plan features:
— Four bedrooms
— Two full and one half baths

■ A sky-lit foyer

■ A sunken Family Room warmed by a fireplace and separated by a railing from the Breakfast Nook

■ A well-appointed Kitchen which serves either the informal Breakfast Nook or the formal Dining Room with efficiency

■ A Master Suite with a walk-in closet, full bath and a private, hidden sun deck

FIRST FLOOR — 1,104 SQ. FT.
SECOND FLOOR — 845 SQ. FT.
GARAGE & WORKSHOP — 538 SQ. FT.
BASEMENT — 1,098 SQ. FT.
WIDTH — 55'-0"
DEPTH — 32'-0"

TOTAL LIVING AREA:
1,949 SQ. FT.

No. 90933

A Westhome Planners, Ltd. Design

No. 90601
Varied Roof Heights Create Interesting Lines

■ This plan features:
— Three bedrooms
— Two full and one half baths

■ A spacious Family Room with a heat-circulating fireplace, which is visible from the Foyer

■ A large Kitchen with a cooktop island, opening into the dinette bay

■ A Master Suite with his-n-her closets and a private Master Bath

■ Two additional bedrooms which share a full hall bath

■ Formal Dining and Living Rooms, flowing into each other for easy entertaining

MAIN AREA — 1,613 SQ. FT.

TOTAL LIVING AREA:
1,613 SQ. FT.

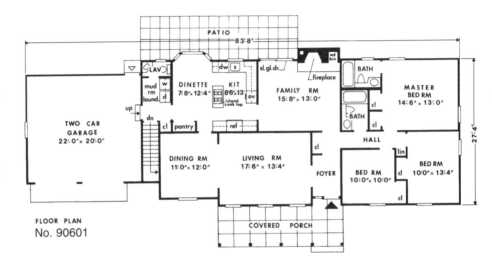

FLOOR PLAN
No. 90601

No. 90941
Vaulted Sunken Living Room

■ This plan features:
— Four bedrooms
— Two full and one half baths

■ A dramatic, sunken Living Room with a vaulted ceiling, fireplace, and glass walls to enjoy the view

■ A well-appointed, Kitchen with a peninsula counter and direct access to the Family Room, Dining Room or the sun deck

■ A Master Suite with a walk-in closet and a private full bath

■ A Family Room with direct access to the rear sun deck

FIRST FLOOR — 1,464 SQ. FT.
BASEMENT FLOOR— 1,187 SQ. FT.
GARAGE — 418 SQ. FT.

TOTAL LIVING AREA:
2,651 SQ. FT.

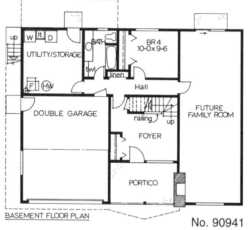

BASEMENT FLOOR PLAN

No. 90941

A Westhome Planners, Ltd. Design

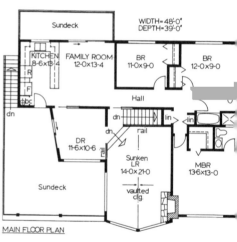

MAIN FLOOR PLAN

No. 91797
Country Ranch

■ This plan features:
— Three bedrooms
— Two full baths

■ A railed and covered wrap-around porch, adding charm to this country-styled home

■ A high vaulted ceiling in the Living Room

■ A smaller Kitchen with ample cupboard and counter space, that is augmented by a large pantry

■ An informal Family Room with access to the wood deck

■ A private Master Suite with a spa tub and a walk-in closet

■ Two family bedrooms that share a full hall bath

■ A shop and storage area in the two-car garage

MAIN AREA — 1,485 SQ. FT.
GARAGE — 701 SQ. FT.

TOTAL LIVING AREA:
1,485 SQ. FT.

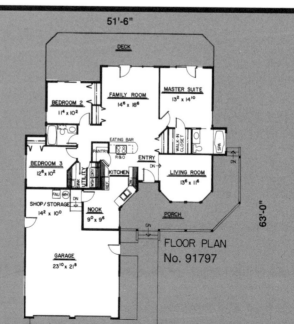

FLOOR PLAN
No. 91797

No. 93269
Cozy Front Porch

■ This plan features:

— Three bedrooms

— Two full and one half bath

■ A Living Room enhanced by a large fireplace

■ A formal Dining Room that is open to the Living Room, giving a more spacious feel to the rooms

■ An efficient Kitchen that includes ample counter and cabinet space as well as double sinks and pass thru window to living area

■ A sunny Breakfast Area with vaulted ceiling and a door to the sun deck

■ A first floor Master Suite with separate tub & shower stall and walk-in closet

■ A first floor powder room with a hide-away laundry center

■ Two additional bedrooms that share a full hall bath

FIRST FLOOR — 1,045 SQ. FT.

SECOND FLOOR — 690 SQ. FT.

BASEMENT — 465 SQ. FT.

GARAGE — 580 SQ. FT.

A Jannis Vann & Associates, Inc. Design

TOTAL LIVING AREA:
1,735 SQ. FT.

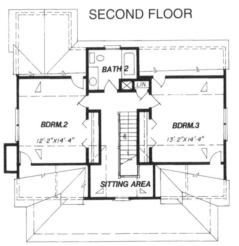

SECOND FLOOR

BATH 2

LIN.

BDRM.2
12'-2"X14'-4"

BDRM.3
13'-2"X14'-4"

SITTING AREA

SUNDECK
16'-0"X12'-0"

BREAKFAST
9'-0"X7'-8"

KIT.
9'-0"X9'-6"

DINING
10'-0"X11'-4"

LIVING AREA
18'-0"X13'-6"

M.BDRM.
15'-6"X13'-6"

PORCH

32'-0"

40'-4"

FIRST FLOOR
No. 93269

No. 10670
Three Fireplaces Add Coziness & Warmth

■ This plan features:
— Five bedrooms
— Four and one half baths
■ Vaulted ceilings, a gently curving staircase and arched windows create an airy feeling of light and space
■ Large island Kitchen opens into a cheery Eating Nook
■ The Family Room includes a fireplace, room-sized wetbar and direct access to a backyard patio
■ A Master Bedroom, warmed by a fireplace, has French doors leading to a personal patio
■ Three additional bedrooms, located on the second floor, each with its own walk-in closet

FIRST FLOOR — 2,849 SQ. FT.
SECOND FLOOR — 1,086 SQ. FT.
GARAGE — 721 SQ. FT.

**TOTAL LIVING AREA:
3,935 SQ. FT.**

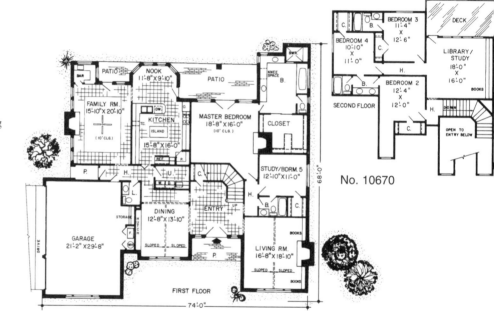

No. 10670

No. 24326
Fireplace-Equipped Family Room

■ This plan features:
— Four bedrooms
— Two full baths and one half bath
■ A lovely front porch shading the entrance
■ A spacious Living Room that opens into the Dining Area which flows into the efficient Kitchen
■ A Family Room equipped with a cozy fireplace and sliding glass doors to a patio
■ A Master Suite with a large walk-in closet and a private bath with a step-in shower
■ Three additional bedrooms that share a full hall bath

FIRST FLOOR — 692 SQ. FT.
SECOND FLOOR — 813 SQ. FT.
BASEMENT — 699 SQ. FT.
GARAGE — 484 SQ. FT.

**TOTAL LIVING AREA:
1,505 SQ. FT.
PROOFED**

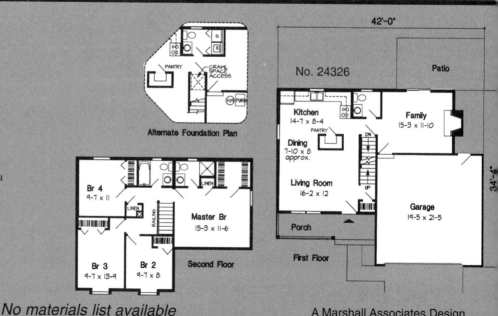

No. 24326

No materials list available

A Marshall Associates Design

No. 34077
Expandable Home

■ This plan features:
— Four bedrooms
— Three full baths

■ Front Entry into open Living Room highlighted by double window

■ Bright Dining area with sliding glass door to optional Patio

■ Compact, efficient Kitchen with peninsula serving/snackbar, laundry closet and outdoor access

■ Two first floor bedrooms with ample closet share a full bath

■ Second floor Master Bedroom and additional bedroom feature dormer windows, private baths and walk-in closets

FIRST FLOOR — 957 SQ. FT.
SECOND FLOOR — 800 SQ. FT.
FOUNDATION —
BASEMENT, SLAB OR CRAWL SPACE

TOTAL LIVING AREA:
1,757 SQ. FT.

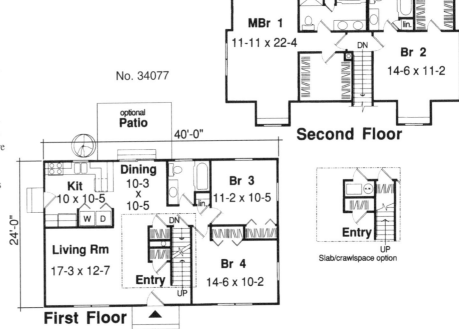

No. 34077

Second Floor

MBr 1
11-11 x 22-4

Br 2
14-6 x 11-2

First Floor

optional Patio
40'-0"
24'-0"

Kit
10 x 10-5

Dining
10-3 x 10-5

Br 3
11-2 x 10-5

Living Rm
17-3 x 12-7

W D

Entry

Br 4
14-6 x 10-2

Entry
UP
Slab/crawlspace option

No. 34926
Compact, yet Elegant

■ This plan features:
— Three bedrooms
— Two and one half baths

■ An angular plan giving each room an interesting shape

■ A wrap-around veranda

■ An entry foyer leading through the Living Room and Parlor

■ A Dining Room with a hexagonal, recessed ceiling

■ A sunny Breakfast room off the island Kitchen

■ A Master Suite with a bump-out window, a walk-in closet, and double sinks in the private bath

FIRST FLOOR — 1,409 SQ. FT.
SECOND FLOOR — 1,116 SQ. FT.
BASEMENT — 1,409 SQ. FT.
GARAGE — 483 SQ. FT.

TOTAL LIVING AREA:
2,525 SQ. FT.

A Karl Kreeger Design

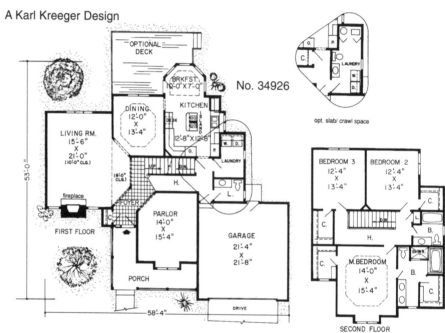

No. 34901
Covered Porch on Farm Style Traditional

■ This plan features:
— Three bedrooms
— Two and one half baths

■ A Dining Room with bay window and an elevated ceiling

■ A Living Room complete with a wood burning stove

■ A two-car Garage

■ Ample storage space throughout the home

FIRST FLOOR — 909 SQ. FT
SECOND FLOOR — 854 SQ. FT.
BASEMENT — 899 SQ. FT.
GARAGE — 491 SQ. FT.

TOTAL LIVING AREA:
1,763 SQ. FT.

A Karl Kreeger Design

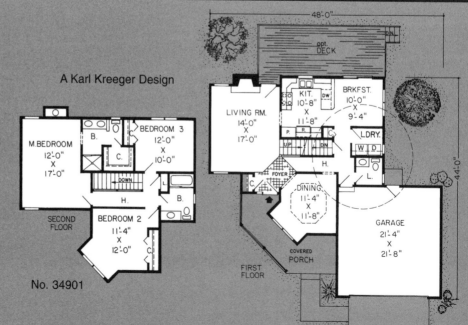

No. 20093
Porch Adorns Elegant Bay

■ This plan features:

—Three bedrooms

—Two and one half baths

■ A Master Suite with romantic bay window and full Bath

■ Bedrooms with huge closets and use of the hall full bath

■ A roomy island Kitchen with modern, efficient layout

■ A Formal Dining Room with recessed decorative ceiling

■ Sloping sky lit ceilings illuminating the fireplaced Living Room

■ A rear Deck accessible from both the Kitchen and the Living Room

FIRST FLOOR — 1,027 SQ. FT.

SECOND FLOOR — 974 SQ. FT.

GARAGE — 476 SQ. FT.

TOTAL LIVING AREA:
2,001 SQ. FT.

SECOND FLOOR

BEDROOM 10'-6"x11'-4"

BEDROOM 10'-8"x11'-6"

HALL

MASTER BEDROOM 11'-0" x 21'-2"

BATH

1/2 WALL

No. 20093

A Karl Kreeger Design

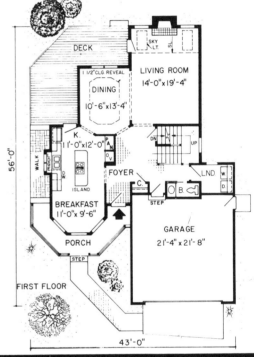

FIRST FLOOR

DECK

DINING 10'-6"x13'-4"

LIVING ROOM 14'-0"x19'-4"

K. 11'-0"x12'-0"

BREAKFAST 11'-0"x 9'-6"

FOYER

GARAGE 21'-4" x 21'-8"

PORCH

56'-0"

43'-0"

You've Picked Your Dream Home!

You can already see it standing on your lot... you can see yourselves in your new home... enjoying family, entertaining guests, celebrating holidays. All that remains ahead are the details. That's where we can help. Whether you plan to build-it-yourself, be your own contractor, or hand your plans over to an outside contractor, your Garlinghouse blueprints provide the perfect beginning for putting yourself in your dream home right away.

We even make it simple for you to make professional design modifications. We can also provide a materials list for greater economy.

My grandfather, L.F. Garlinghouse, started a tradition of quality when he founded this company in 1907. For over 85 years, homeowners and builders have relied on us for accurate, complete, professional blueprints. Our plans help you get results fast... and save money, too! These pages will give you all the information you need to order. So get started now... I know you'll love your new Garlinghouse home!

Sincerely,

TYPICAL WALL SECTION

SEE ELEVATIONS
1" AIRSPACE CLEARANCE ABOVE INSULATION
COMPOSITION SHINGLES OVER 15# FELT OVER 1/2" CDX PLYWOOD
METAL DRIP EDGE
GUTTER & DOWNSPOUT
1x FASCIA OVER 2x SUBFASCIA
2x4 LOOKOUTS @ 24" O.C.
3/8" EXT. PLYWOOD SOFFIT W/ 2" CONTINUOUS SCREENED VENT OR 4" x 16" SCREENED METAL VENTS @ 48" O.C.
2x CONT. LOOKOUT BACKER
STEEL ANGLE LINTEL
TRIM: SEE ELEVATIONS
WINDOWS: SEE FLOOR PLAN
1/2" CDX PLYWOOD SHEATHING W/ OPTIONAL R-5 INSULATION BOARD OVER
WEATHER PROOF BARRIER TYP. ALL GEOGRAPHICAL AREAS
VAPOR BARRIER WHERE APPLICABLE
MASONRY VENEER W/ GALV. TIES @ 16" O.C. HORIZONTALLY INTO STUDS AND 16" O.C. VERT.
1" AIR SPACE
WEEP HOLES @ 24" O.C.
6" MIN FROM BOTTOM MOST WOOD TO GRADE
METAL FLASHING
SLOPE GRADE AWAY FROM FOUNDATION 6" IN FIRST 10' (TYP)

12

2x @ 16" O.C. SEE FRAMING PLANS (TYP.)
R-30 INSULATION (MIN.)
1/2" GYP. BD. CEILING
(2) 2x4 TOP PLATES MIN. LAP 48"
(2) 2x12 HEADER @ EXT. & BEARING WALLS (TYP.) U.N.O.
WINDOW TRIM (TYP.)
WOOD STOOL & TRIM
2x4 STUDS @ 16" O.C. W/ R-13 BATT INSULATION OPTIONAL CONSTRUCTION
2x6 STUDS @ 16" O.C. W/ R-19 BATT INSULATION VERIFY WITH ENERGY REPORT WHERE APPLICABLE
1/2" GYP. BD. WALLS
BASE TRIM
BOTTOM PLATE
FOUNDATION: SEE FOUNDATION PLAN
FIN. GRADE @ HOUSE WALL

This section is provided to help your builder understand the structural components and materials used to construct the exterior walls of your home. This section will address insulation, roof components, and interior and exterior wall finishes. Your plans will be designed with either 2x4 or 2x6 exterior walls, but most professional contractors can easily adapt the plans to the wall thickness you require.

EXTERIOR ELEVATIONS

REAR ELEVATION
SCALE: 1/8" = 1'-0"

LEFT SIDE ELEVATION
SCALE: 1/8" = 1'-0"

Elevations are scaled drawings of the front, rear, left and right sides of a home. All of the necessary information pertaining to the exterior finish materials, roof pitches and exterior height dimensions of your home are defined.

CABINET PLANS

W2430 FILLER W2430 W3015 W2430 FILLER
W3030 CB36 D.W. CB36 W3624
B9 SF36 RANGE B15
FILLER AS NEEDED
W3615 KITCHEN B36 W3624
REF B36 W3624

KITCHEN CABINET PLAN
SCALE: 3/8" = 1'-0"

These plans, or in some cases elevations, will detail the layout of the kitchen and bathroom cabinets at a larger scale. This gives you an accurate layout for your cabinets or an ideal starting point for a modified custom cabinet design.

ake Your Dream Come True!

for home designs by respected professionals.

FIREPLACE DETAILS

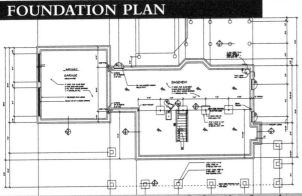

If the home you have chosen includes a fireplace, the fireplace detail will show typical methods to construct the firebox, hearth and flue chase for masonry units, or a wood frame chase for a zero-clearance unit.

TYPICAL CROSS SECTION

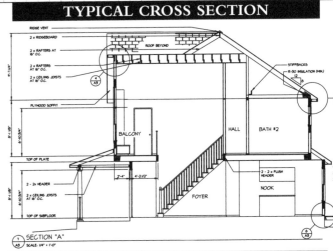

A cut-away cross-section through the entire home shows your building contractor the exact correlation of construction components at all levels of the house. It will help to clarify the load bearing points from the roof all the way down to the basement.

FOUNDATION PLAN

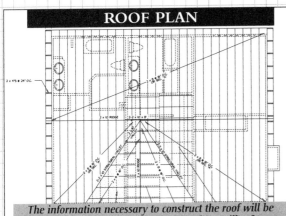

These plans will accurately dimension the footprint of your home including load bearing points and beam placement if applicable. The foundation style will vary from plan to plan. Your local climatic conditions will dictate whether a basement, slab or crawlspace is best suited for your area. In most cases, if your plan comes with one foundation style, a professional contractor can easily adapt the foundation plan to an alternate style.

DETAILED FLOOR PLANS

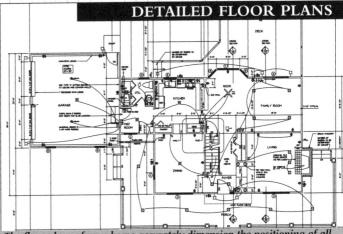

The floor plans of your home accurately dimension the positioning of all walls, doors, windows, stairs and permanent fixtures. They will show you the relationship and dimensions of rooms, closets and traffic patterns. Included is the schematic of the electrical layout. This layout is clearly represented and does not hinder the clarity of other pertinent information shown. All these details will help your builder properly construct your new home.

ROOF PLAN

The information necessary to construct the roof will be included with your home plans. Some plans will reference roof trusses, while many others contain schematic framing plans. These framing plans will indicate the lumber sizes necessary for the rafters and ridgeboards based on the designated roof loads.

STAIR DETAILS

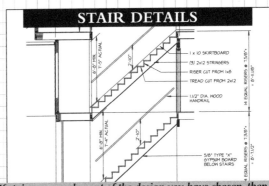

If stairs are an element of the design you have chosen, then a cross-section of the stairs will be included in your home plans. This gives your builders the essential reference points that they need for headroom clearance, and riser and tread dimensions.

GARLINGHOUSE OPTIONS & EXTRAS
MAKE THE DREAM TRULY YOURS.

Reversed Plans Can Make Your Dream Home Just Right!

"That's our dream home... if only the garage were on the other side!"

You could have exactly the home you want by flipping it end-for-end. Check it out by holding your dream home page of this book up to a mirror. Then simply order your plans "reversed". We'll send you one full set of mirror-image plans (with the writing backwards) as a master guide for you and your builder.

The remaining sets of your order will come as shown in this book so the dimensions and specifications are easily read on the job site... but they will be specially stamped "REVERSED" so there is no construction confusion.

We can only send reversed plans with multiple-set orders. But, there is no extra charge for this service.

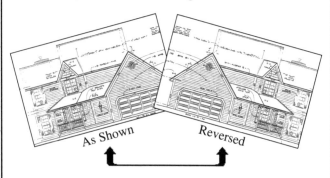

As Shown   Reversed

Modifying Your Garlinghouse Home Plan

Easy modifications to your dream home such as minor non-structural changes and simple material substitutions, can be made between you and your builder and marked directly on your blueprints. However, if you are considering making major changes to your design, we strongly recommend that you purchase our reproducible vellums and use the services of a professional designer or architect. For additional information call us at 1-860-343-5977.

Our Reproducible Vellums Make Modifications Easier

With a vellum copy of our plans, a design professional can alter the drawings just the way you want, then you can print as many copies of the modified plans as you need. And, since you have already started with our complete detailed plans, the cost of those expensive professional services will be significantly less. Refer to the price schedule for vellum costs. Call for vellum availability for plan numbers 90,000 and above.

Reproducible vellum copies of our home plans are only sold under the terms of a license agreement that you will receive with your order. Should you not agree to the terms, then the vellums may be returned unopened for a full refund.

Yours FREE With Your Order
FREE
SPECIFICATIONS AND CONTRACT FORM

provides the perfect way for you and your builder to agree on the exact materials to use in building and finishing your home before you start construction. A must for homeowner's peace of mind.

Remember To Order Your Materials List

It'll help you save money. Available at a modest additional charge, the Materials List gives the quantity, dimensions, and specifications for the major materials needed to build your home. You will get faster, more accurate bids from your contractors and building suppliers — and avoid paying for unused materials and waste. Materials Lists are available for all home plans except as otherwise indicated, but can only be ordered with a set of home plans. Due to differences in regional requirements and homeowner or builder preferences... electrical, plumbing and heating/air conditioning equipment specifications are not designed specifically for each plan. However, non plan specific detailed typical prints of residential electrical, plumbing and construction guidelines can be provided. Please see next page for additional information.

Questions?

Call our customer service number at 1-860-343-5977.

How Many Sets Of Plans Will You Need?

The Standard 8-Set Construction Package

Our experience shows that you'll speed every step of construction and avoid costly building errors by ordering enough sets to go around. Each tradesperson wants a set — the general contractor and all subcontractors; foundation, electrical, plumbing, heating/air conditioning, drywall, finish carpenters, and cabinet shop. Don't forget your lending institution, building department and, of course, a set for yourself.

The Minimum 5-Set Construction Package

If you're comfortable with arduous follow-up, this package can save you a few dollars by giving you the option of passing down plan sets as work progresses. You might have enough copies to go around if work goes exactly as scheduled and no plans are lost or damaged. But for only $50 more, the 8-set package eliminates these worries.

The Single-Set Decision-Maker Package

We offer this set so you can study the blueprints to plan your dream home in detail. But remember... one set is never enough to build your home... and they're copyrighted.

New Plan Details For The Home Builder

Because local codes and requirements vary greatly, we recommend that you obtain drawings and bids from licensed contractors to do your mechanical plans. However, if you want to know more about techniques — and deal more confidently with subcontractors — we offer these remarkably useful detail sheets. Each is an excellent tool that will enhance your understanding of these technical subjects.

Residential Construction Details

Eight sheets that cover the essentials of stick-built residential home construction. Details foundation options - poured concrete basement, concrete block, or monolithic concrete slab. Shows all aspects of floor, wall, and roof framing. Provides details for roof dormers, eaves, and skylights. Conforms to requirements of Uniform Building code or BOCA code. Includes a quick index.

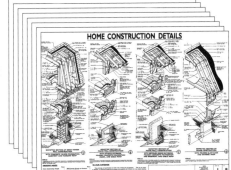

$14.95 per set

Residential Plumbing Details

Nine sheets packed with information detailing pipe connection methods, fittings, and sizes. Shows sump-pump and water softener hookups, and septic system construction. Conforms to requirements of National Plumbing Code. Color coded with a glossary of terms and quick index.

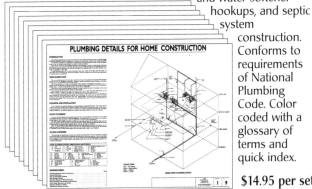

$14.95 per set

Residential Electrical Details

Nine sheets that cover all aspects of residential wiring, from simple switch wiring to the complexities of three-phase and service entrance connection. Explains service load calculations and distribution panel wiring. Shows you how to create a floor-plan wiring diagram. Conforms to requirements of National Electrical Code. Color coded with a glossary of terms and a quick index.

$14.95 per set

Important Shipping Information

Please refer to the shipping charts on the order form for service availability for your specific plan number. Our delivery service must have a street address or Rural Route Box number — never a post office box. Use a work address if no one is home during the day.

Orders being shipped to APO, FPO or Post Office Boxes must go via First Class Mail. Please include the proper postage.

For our International Customers, only Certified bank checks and money orders are accepted and must be payable in U.S. currency. For speed, we ship international orders Air Parcel Post. Please refer to the chart for the correct shipping cost.

An important note:

All plans are drawn to conform to one or more of the industry's major national building standards. However, due to the variety of local building regulations, your plan may need to be modified to comply with local requirements — snow loads, energy loads, seismic zones, etc. Do check them fully and consult your local building officials.

A few states require that all building plans used be drawn by an architect registered in that state. While having your plans reviewed and stamped by such an architect may be prudent, laws requiring non-conforming plans like ours to be completely redrawn forces you to unnecessarily pay very large fees. If your state has such a law, we strongly recommend you contact your state representative to protest.

Please submit all Canadian plan orders to:
Garlinghouse Company
60 Baffin Place, Unit #5, Waterloo, Ontario N2V 1Z7
Canadian Customers Only: 1-800-561-4169/Fax #: 1-800-719-3291
Customer Service #: 1-519-746-4169

Please have ready: **1. Your credit card number 2. The plan number 3. The order code number** ⇨ **H6BS8**

ORDER TOLL FREE— 1-800-235-5700
Monday-Friday 8:00 a.m. to 5:00 p.m. Eastern Time
or FAX your Credit Card order to 1-860-343-5984
All foreign residents call 1-860-343-5977

GARLINGHOUSE 1996 BLUEPRINT PRICE SCHEDULE:

Additional sets with original order $25

TOTAL LIVING AREA	0000-1500 sq. ft.	1501-1800 sq. ft.	1801-2200 sq. ft.	2201-2600 sq. ft.	2601-3200 sq. ft.	3201-9999 sq. ft.
8 SETS OF SAME PLAN	$330	$350	$375	$400	$430	$470
5 SETS OF SAME PLAN	$280	$300	$325	$350	$380	$420
1 SINGLE SET OF PLANS	$210	$230	$255	$280	$310	$350
VELLUMS	$420	$440	$465	$490	$520	$560
MATERIALS LIST	$25	$25	$30	$30	$35	$40

SHIPPING & HANDLING ALL PLANS

	1-3 Sets	4-6 Sets	7+ & Vellums
First Class Mail(5-7 Days)*P.O. Boxes Only	$9.00	$18.00	$20.00
Regular Delivery Canada(7-10 Days)	$14.00	$17.00	$20.00
Express Delivery Canada(5-6 Days)	$35.00	$40.00	$45.00
Overseas Delivery Airmail(2-3 Weeks)	$45.00	$52.00	$60.00

SHIPPING (Plans 1-89999)

	1-3 Sets	4-6 Sets	7+ & Vellums
Standard Delivery(UPS 2-Day)	$15.00	$20.00	$25.00
Overnight Delivery	$30.00	$35.00	$40.00

SHIPPING (Plans 90000-99000)

	1-3 Sets	4-6 Sets	7+ & Vellums
Ground Delivery(7-10 Days)	$9.00	$18.00	$20.00
Express Delivery(3-5 Days)	$15.00	$20.00	$25.00

Canadian Orders and Shipping: To our friends in Canada, we have a plan design affiliate in Kitchener, Ontario. This relationship will help you avoid the delays and charges associated with shipments from the United States. Moreover, our affiliate is familiar with the building requirements in your community and country. We prefer payments in U.S. Currency. If you, however, are sending Canadian funds please add 40% to the prices of the plans and shipping fees.

GARLINGHOUSE — Blueprint Order Form — Order Code No. **H6BS8**

Plan No. _____

☐ As Shown   ☐ Reversed *(mult. set pkgs. only)*

	Each	Amount
8 set pkg.		$
5 set pkg.		$
1 set pkg. (no reverses)		$
_____ (qty.) Add'l. sets @ $25 each		$
Vellums		$
Materials List (with plan order only)		$
Residential Builder Plans (not plan specific)		
_____ set(s) Construction	@ $14.95	$
_____ set(s) Plumbing	@ $14.95	$
_____ set(s) Electrical	@ $14.95	$
Shipping		$
Subtotal		$
Sales Tax (CT residents add 6% sales tax, KS residents add 6.15% sales tax-not required for other states)		$
Total Amount Enclosed		**$**

Prices guaranteed until 8-16-97
Payment must be made in U.S. funds
Foreign Mail Orders: Certified bank checks in U.S. funds only

Credit Card Information

Charge To:	☐ Visa	☐ Mastercard

Card # ☐☐☐☐ ☐☐☐☐ ☐☐☐☐ ☐☐☐☐

Signature _____ Exp. ____/____

Send your check, money order or credit card information to:
(No C.O.D.'s Please)

Please Submit all <u>United States</u> & <u>Other Nations</u> plan orders to:
Garlinghouse Company
P.O. Box 1717
Middletown, CT 06457

Please Submit all <u>Canadian</u> plan orders to:
Garlinghouse Company
60 Baffin Place, Unit #5
Waterloo, Ontario N2V 1Z7

Bill To: (address must be as it appears on credit card statement)

Name _____

Address _____

City/State _____ Zip _____

Daytime Phone (____) _____

Ship To (if different from Bill to):

Name _____

Address _____

City/State _____ Zip _____

TERMS OF SALE FOR HOME PLANS: